P9-EJI-921

FIC K33 5
Kene   Thomas.
Mos   lawgiver

Date Due

COLUMBIA BIBLE COLLEGE
4444 00001 5875

COLUMBIA BIBLE COLLEGE
LIBRARY 87-22251
CLEARBROOK, B.C.

From,
Wayne

MOSES
THE LAWGIVER

MOSES
THE LAWGIVER

Thomas Keneally

HARPER & ROW,
PUBLISHERS

NEW YORK, EVANSTON,
SAN FRANCISCO, LONDON

© RAI/ITC – Incorporated Television Company Ltd
and Thomas Keneally 1975

All rights reserved. Printed in Great Britain. No part of this
book may be used or reproduced in any manner whatsoever without
permission except in the case of brief quotations embodied in
critical articles and reviews. For information address Harper & Row,
Publishers, Inc., 10 East 53rd Street, New York, N.Y. 10022.

First U.S. edition
ISBN: 0–06–064773–6
Library of Congress Catalog Card Number: 75–9322

Contents

The Lawgiver meets a Miner from Crete

I knew the man, but only from the morning he caught me looking for copper in the Wilderness of Zin.

It went like this. My native island is Crete. It was there I got my training in metals. I came to the Nile delta in a ship of which I was part owner. I wanted to see the sights, of course. Memphis, Thebes, the pyramids and the rest of it. Travelling upstream by barge I met a high official from the Pharaoh's Metals Office. Since it's not my story but the man's, I'll be brief.

Enough to say I was taken to an audience with Pharaoh Rameses, quizzed by experts, and offered the management of the copper mines in the Peninsula of Zin. I was promised a garrison and a nice house. At the time of the offer I was in Avaris, the new town Rameses had thrown up for his glory in the Nile delta. It didn't have the class of the older Egyptian cities – the statuary was lumpy, the palace façade looked vulgar. Too much slave labour (Libyan, Nubian, Hapiru) had gone into it, not enough craftsmanship. I thought, I suppose my nice villa in Zin will be rough as guts.

But the offer I was made! I got a percentage royalty that rose according to output. This was an amazing arrangement, especially in a nation that believed that all minerals belonged to Pharaoh by divine law, because he was a son of the god who had put them in the earth.

On the day I was captured I had been sampling ore in the plateau area of Zin, a little south of the camel track to Arabia. It was quite early in the morning and I'd left my camp with only one man to carry my instruments. I went tapping along the ridge with a pick. It really was as lifeless a place as you could see. You found it hard to believe it even had insects. Though of course it had. A scorpion under every rock.

You're not looking for life out there. You don't expect to see it. When you do it distracts you. Now, the wind was at my back when I walked over the ridge and there below me were tents and asses, raggedy sheep, and men talking to each other (though the sound of their talk and everything else was being blown away from me by a fierce wind) and some women sitting pretty listless on the shady sides of the tents.

Even at that first sight they didn't look like an ordinary tribe. There must have been two thousand – more than the route they were travelling was meant to support. No wonder the women were listless. All tribal wisdom, all knowledge of water sources, argued against bringing two thousand people into that place.

So I stood too long wondering about what I saw – about three seconds in all. And I was seen. Half a dozen young men – a sort of watch they had, lean boys, rather taller than Egyptians – rode out of the camp on asses. It was as if they'd been waiting for just such a fool as me to appear on the skyline.

I ran back down the ridge towards the place where my man had the two camels tethered. I kept slipping in scree. Those tribes do dreadful things to civilised people, put them in a bag of scorpions, suspend them by the genitals. That's a tribe of fifty. I did not want to find out what a tribe of two thousand could do.

When my man saw the tribesmen on asses top the ridge and ride after me he did not hesitate. He spurred his own camel and slapped mine and galloped away south. The way I ran and the obscenities I yelled! I was hit by a stick from behind, I lay half-conscious tasting that sour earth. They sat me up.

I didn't know it, but the black-haired young savage who then questioned me was, at the time, the leader of a sort of crude police force. He would one day be a general and, one day again, a king. Called Joshua.

They spoke Aramaic, the language the slaves at the mine spoke. I had no idea they were, themselves, escaped slaves.

I said, 'The Pharaoh would buy me back for a lot of money. I am his superintendent of mines.'

The boy said, 'There are mines close by?'

'Well, yes. I mean . . . just a bit that way. The way my wretched servant went.'

'Garrisons at the mines?'

'Yes, garrisons. That's why I say: sell me back.'

At the word garrisons they all looked at each other.

Joshua put a noose round my neck and they dragged me over the ridge and down into the camp. Amongst the tents children and women followed me.

'Where am I going?' I asked. My voice broke on the question.

'To see the Representative.'

'The Representative?' I giggled – concussed, sun-struck, stupid. 'Who does he represent?'

The boy did not answer.

So I was taken to a particular tent that a man had all to himself – there was not a sign of his women or children. It turned out *they* were waiting for him in another place. But I thought how funny it was that a chieftain didn't have at least a couple of girls around.

When I saw the occupant, he was sitting quietly on a bed-roll in a corner. He stood. He was tall. He had an impediment. As if one side of his tongue was paralysed. He didn't look like the hairy sheik I'd expected.

Now if I belonged to the gushing school of writers I would say, as they do, that fire came from his eyes. But I wasn't looking at his eyes. I was looking at the floor and whimpering a little.

Joshua briefed the headman. You could tell the boy was very happy, doing this sort of work. For the tribe, for this man. One day he might want to be chief but he was happy for the time being.

'Garrisons,' the man said in his weird way. He leant down to my ear. 'You'll have to come with us. You won't be hurt.

My heart opened like a flower. I began panting as a dog does.

'But, my lord, I know the area. If you stay here you can't water your tribe. If you move east you can't, and west is bad too. Take me south and I will see you're watered at the mines, and let you have pasturage. Unmolested.'

'We can't go there. Besides, we have a guarantee of clear water.'

'I *do* hope so, sir.' I spoke up because I thought, if I'm made to travel across Zin with two thousand people, we're all going to die. 'I can't help wondering who guarantees water to you in this part of the world.'

'There is Yahweh. The Guarantor.'

'Yahweh, you say?' The name sounded suspiciously like the name of a tribal god.

'He-Who-Is,' the man said, chewing the words up. 'I am his Representative.''

I couldn't help liking him. His stoop, his slow talk. Then I saw it. I could tell by his stance. He was Egyptian. Now I felt at home. I adopted the gentlemen-amongst-oafs tone – 'We two understand each other, etc.' But he wouldn't turn south. He wouldn't sell me back to Pharaoh.

He answered me only when I said I'd been the dinner-guest both of Rameses and the new Pharaoh, Merneptak.

He said, 'Did you ever meet Princess Aniva-Hathi?'

As a matter of fact I did remember her. A starved-looking lady. Scars on her arms where surgeons had been at her. You remembered her for her conspicuous sickness.

'She was . . . my step-mother,' he said.

'My lord,' I said.

His name was an Egyptian name, or the stump of one. It may even have been Rameses or Amon-eses, according to the Egyptian custom of putting the name of a god before the human name. His name now, amongst his people, was Meses – he had cut the god bit out of it. The tribesmen mispronounced it – Moses and Moishe. I myself called him Moses, all the years I knew him.

I was a very good friend of his. Of course, I am not mentioned in the legends. I have a foreign background, and am often flippant. I argue with some of the figures and some of the claims. Although, after seven years, I lay down and let a priest cut my foreskin off, I am not liked by priests or writers.

Now, everyone believes the man was born of Hapiru (that is, Hebrew) slaves working on the new town of Pithom near the delta, and that he got adopted into the royal household and was merely *raised* as an Egyptian. The theme is: the poor boy who is accidently educated as a prince in the household of the king and then returns to his true relatives to set them free from the king.

All I say about it is that this theme occurs a lot in stories about heroes. It comes in handy when you want to show that Moses, the liberator, wasn't a member of the hated race.

If I point all this out, people think I'm trying to be irreverent. In fact, it's very likely the man *was* Hebrew by birth. On the day I was captured, there was a man and a woman in the camp who *believed* he was their brother by blood. This man and this woman, Aaron and Miriam by name, were simply escaped slaves. Why should they believe so stubbornly he was their blood brother?

Poor old Miriam died in the desert of a haemorrhage. Before she died, her version of how Moses was born and saved from the crocodiles became part of everyone's picture of the man. Here it is, filled out by what I know myself about Egyptian life and politics.

Miriam's people (Moses' people?) had been tribal herders to the east of the Nile delta. The Egyptians called them Hapiru and pitied them for being un-washed and coarse. They'd probably been let over the border two hundred years earlier. The area where they grazed their stock was called the Land of Goshen. It was good grassland. Though the Egyptians pitied them their rough life in tents, they were better off than many Egyptian farmers. They ate meat, papyrus shoots and onions. They fished in back waters of the great river, but their camps were generally a fair way from the Nile, for they feared mosquitoes, vipers (Moses *was* very frightened of vipers) and crocodiles.

They had a tribal god to whom they sacrificed animals. They used to call him the Old One. I found out at the risk of my own flesh that in some of these people there was a lingering taste for sacrificing humans. But you'll hear about that later.

Pharaoh Rameses decided very early that he wanted the Hapiru rounded up. I can imagine him deciding on it. Perhaps at midnight, because he liked working at night. He often kept his cabinet up five nights a week, never mind wives and girl-friends. He spoke in a jerky way, very unearthly. Whether that was an impediment or a means of bluffing people at night council meetings, who could say? But it *was* very like the way Moses talked. Family connections? I only raise the question, no more.

Now, one of the larger events of Pharaoh Rameses' young life was the day that, at Megiddo in Palestine, he had been ambushed with his forward units by the Hittite army. He had fought his way out of the encirclement. After that he always feared an invasion from the north. If there was a war it was likely that all those quick-breeding Hapiru would side with the invader. They had racial and religious reasons for it.

To go with his fear, Rameses had a need for cheap workers. He rebuilt numerous towns, especially round the delta. There was a lust for building in him. It was a disease. Once I saw the giant statues he had built above the First Cataract to awe the natives. In my opinion that's about all some of his building was good for. If there was a building that wasn't actually a national monument, down it went. More floor space for his mania. If the building *was* revered and not condemned by engineers, he had it covered with stone scroll-work mainly on the same theme: How I, Rameses, dealt with the Hittites at Megiddo.

So he had two reasons for enslaving Hapiru. It took a long time to find them all and get them into work camps.

There was a work camp near Pithom. Miriam, who, as I say, believed she was Moses' sister, came there as a child. She was brought there with her father Amram, her mother Yokabed, and a young brother called Aaron. They had been tribesmen in a clan called Levi of a tribe called Israel. They had had all Goshen to wander in. Now they were crammed into a one-room barracks where there were already three slave families. The three wives in possession fought a lot with Yokabed at first about the use of the utensils and the fire. But in the end they had to make friends with her.

Amram was a mere muscle slave, hauling stone from the river to Pithom. I've seen slaves at such work. On shifty ground where wagons would get bogged down they put rollers under the stones and hundreds of men to drag on the ropes. Hard yes, but if you can stand it it makes you fit. And, as a matter of policy, the food is good.

There were troubles. Overcrowding in the barracks. The sewers over-flowing and lapping at the doorsteps. Diseases of the eyes in the babies that lived. Lack of freedom of movement (which is harder on a pastoral people than on others). And the lash was used by foremen (some of them Hapiru) according to whim. Still, compare this life with the lives of some peasants, and it stood up well.

Pithom camp seems to have been an average camp. The old men who had been there a long time often said so.

'The Egyptians are good managers. They don't like messy camps. The only thing you have to be scared of is the size of their stones.'

They were thinking of the risk of being crushed like a gnat. When you use crowds of slaves to move lumps of rock as large as villas you depend on ropes and pulleys. You depend on human sense and on men not tripping. But ropes break, pulleys crash, overseers go on a drunk, men stumble. Under rocks like those a man bursts like a grape and becomes a smear.

The Israelis were a large tribe and it took two camps, Pi-Rameses as well as Pithom, to house their twelve clans. They were used on the building of the two great store cities of the same names. Pi-Rameses stood near one of the river's twelve mouths, and Pithom was forty miles south, on the inland road to Palestine.

The Israelis' clan names were Levi, Benjamin, Gad, Ruben, Asher, Simeon, Judah, Issachar, Zabulon, Dan, Napthali and Manasseh. The god they'd had when they were desert herders wouldn't let them make or wear images of other gods, not even of himself. Now people began to wear ornaments, like the Pillar of Osiris and the Eye of Horus. One day Miriam beat a girl up for wearing one of these. The fight was a long one, and she can remember an old woman calling from a corner, 'Slaves don't beat up slaves.' But Miriam went on punching.

When Miriam was ten her mother got pregnant again. Yokabed had lost two since Aaron was born. But she wasn't downhearted this time. She *knew* (said Miriam) that this one had the aura of a healthy child.

At the time the first of the population laws had been made. Camp life had not diminished the fertility of the Hapiru. Therefore the government instructed all midwives in the camps to kill boy children at birth, until further

notice. Midwives have ways of doing these things. They can strangle the child with its mother's cord, they can smother it with their hands. But they don't like it, unless they're twisted.

The midwife at Pi-Rameses was Phua, an Egyptian. The one at Pithom was called Sephora. They're both well remembered by the Israelis, because they would not enforce the law. And, likewise, midwives nearly everywhere.

When the police spoke to Sephora and Phua and others, the midwives said that Hebrew women know how to give birth on their own rather than call in a midwife who might strangle their child for them. I can imagine Rameses asking his cabinet how they hadn't anticipated this.

'Who can leave the execution of the law to a midwife?' he would have said. 'She is not an arm of government. The army is. The blood of midwives is a bad omen and dishonours Goddess Sekmet, who is a friend to all of them. You cannot therefore behead a disobedient midwife. But a disobedient soldier . . .'

As the child kicked in her belly, Yokabed felt confident the first Population Control Law gave her nothing to fear.

It was the second Population Control Law, made three months before her time, that frightened her. It set up Control Commissioners in all the camps. They had an armed staff. Their brief was: To keep a record of all women approaching term, and when they gave birth to record the date. To record if the child was male or female, and if it were male and lived through the birth to drown it. At Pi-Rameses the river was at hand. At Pithom they fed the children into the tributary stream. The corpses would reach the great river unless they tangled in reeds or were taken by crocodiles.

Miriam tells of boy infants being loaded in a cart in Pithom camp, their legs tied together, as if there was danger of escape. Mothers were forced to stay in the camp – if they tried to follow to the water they were hacked at by the guards, seconded soldiers.

Naturally the guards didn't like the work and so hacked away energetically just to keep the mothers out of their way, just to get the drowning over quickly.

The waterways became terrible places. Sometimes you would see a ghastly little corpse float by. But Pharaoh did not fear his river would be tainted. The river was fat with scavengers. Chief were the revered crocodiles whose savagery honoured Sebek, the crocodile god.

By dressing in a way to conceal the pregnancy, Yokabed avoided being noted down in the Pithom commissioner's roll of women approaching term. She had the help of all the women in her barracks. None of them, only Yokabed, was carrying a child at the time.

Miriam told me that if there were two pregnant women in the one barracks and only one was noted down, the one would start wailing and then inform on the one who'd been missed. Even the women in Yokabed's barracks got tired of protecting her pregnancy.

Women would get her in a corner.

'How are you going to keep him, eh?'

'Well,' Yokabed told them, 'It might be a girl.'

'How will you keep him? His birth's got to be registered you know. Face it, dear. It's hard, but face it.'

'I'll keep him somewhere.'

'Not here. There'll be trouble for all of us if he's found here. We've got husbands and our own children. We don't want them punished for . . .' And they would gesture in the direction of Yokabed's belly.

One night she woke up and began gasping with the onset of labour. Miriam heard it and came and stood over her mother. From other palettes the slaves were hissing, 'Quieten down.' They were afraid the night patrols would hear her yelling in child-birth. Husbands groaned at their wives. 'Get her to shut up. Go on. Hell!'

Amram, the father, was at her ear. 'You have to be brave, dear.' Miriam went on watching. 'Help me,' he told Miriam.

They each took one of Yokabed's elbows and Amram carried her out-of-doors. Amram had clearly observed the pattern of the night patrols and the way the boundaries of the camp were guarded. Because slaves had nowhere to go, there were no walls around any of the camps and, says Miriam, no endless patrolling of the boundaries. Maybe many pregnant women therefore went out of the camp area to give birth secretly. If more did not, I can only put it down to the lack of enterprise you find in slaves after a few generations.

Amram kept telling Miriam. 'I didn't expect it so quickly. There's always been more warning.'

He was a mixture of tender and peevish.

'Not long now, my love. Now, listen. It's no good yelling like that.'

Close to some abandoned barracks stood a shed. It had a jumble of old building tools and a brick cart. Amram put a bed-roll under the cart. Young Miriam acted as midwife to her mother. It was a quick birth. The sac burst and the child was born smeared with blood. But by the light of their lamp they could see he had a boy's sex. This child, Miriam was always certain, grew to be the Egyptian to whom I was brought the day of my capture more than thirty years later in the Wilderness of Zin.

The cart and implements that filled the shed had been left behind when

the nearby slave camp was abandoned. The site was not likely to be visited
by anyone. For three months the child stayed there. Yokabed had to keep
flitting daily back to Pithom camp to create the impression that she was
always there. The authorities who ran the camp would know what it meant
if a woman was away for long stretches.

When *she* wasn't with the baby, Miriam was. He developed an infant rage
against the little girl, because she could give him a lap but no milk.

You have to admit it's a touching story – the god of the crocodiles ravening
for the baby. And mother and sister hiding with it, beneath a brick cart.

Once, when it rained, they heard men-slaves with a day off from brick-
making fishing unhappily along the river bank and arguing whether they
ought to shelter in the nearby shed. But the rain stopped and they moved
away up-river.

The father, Amram, was having a much harder time in barracks. The women would archly say, 'Your wife's away so much.'

'She's seeing a physician,' he'd tell them. 'Since she lost the child there's been these pains . . .'

'When do you think she'll be back to normal?'

'That's a hard question.'

Miriam never told me what the baby's Israeli name was. I don't know why. But now we're at the amazing core of her story.

How the Lawgiver found
a Royal Mother

Rameses' daughter, Aniva-Hathi, the sick, lean girl, was sterile. The Pharaoh always instructed the staff of temples what to ask their gods for, and a month before he signed the law against Hebrew boy-babies he sent a circular to all the temples demanding that Horus, Ra, Taurt the Hippopotamus, Bast of the Cats, Sekhet of the Lionesses, Buto of the Cobras, Nekhbet of the Vultures, Hathi of the fertile Cows and, above all, the great river itself, be asked to provide Princess Aniva-Hathi with a child. And by a child he meant a son.

At Pithom there was a temple to Horus for the use of camp staff and any slaves who fancied the gods of Egypt. In its forecourt the princess's sad situation was announced by priests. (The most ordinary temples had big staffs – at least fifty priests of all grades just to service a slave camp temple!)

Now the weird thing is that it is easy to get ordinary people and even slaves to feel sorry for a princess. Slaves came home from the temple, back into a camp that threatened to burst with seed, and made sympathetic noises about poor Aniva-Hathi, named in the temples by her father as infertile.

The Egyptian priests had said Aniva-Hathi was in disgrace for not bearing babies and exiled to a river villa near Bubastis, only seven miles from the shed. There she washed in milk and doused herself in the fertile river every day.

So Miriam and her mother knew Aniva-Hathi wanted a baby. The girl thought up the scheme. One day when Yokabed arrived at the shed, depressed, breasts stinging with milk, she found Miriam ignoring the wailing child and weaving papyrus reeds.

'What's happening?'

'You'll have to get some tar, Yokabed mother. You'll have to get a little pot for boiling it down.'

'Tar? *A pot?*'

'A little boat,' said Miriam. 'The little man's ship.'

Yokabed said, 'Be quiet. He isn't going away on the river.'

'He'll go away on the river, Yokabed. Dead or in a little boat.'

Yokabed cried at the truth of that. 'What then? You're a heartless girl. Really. What? Down the river in his little basket, till the tar cracks? Or into open seas?'

'We'll leave him floating in the shallows. On the princess's beach.'

'And she'll have him drowned.'

'No.'

'I tell you, yes. A heartless girl you are.'

'Yokabed, Yokabed, she has asked the river for a child. She can't throw back what the river gives her.'

For the first time the idea bit into Yokabed. 'And we lose him for ever. To a royal house. To a royal breast.'

'You'll have to present yourself, mother Yokabed.'

'That isn't easy, girl. Do you think it's easy?'

'No. But if you're there. On the spot . . .'

Yokabed fed and caressed the boy and they argued the plan. As she walked back into Pithom camp that evening she found a woman from another barracks following her. She stopped. The woman made up the distance with short, quick, angry steps.

'Why should you have your boy, bitch? When I don't have mine?'

'I have no boy. Except Aaron, seven years.'

'The boy-*baby*, the boy-*baby*!'

'Do you mean the two that were stillborn?'

'Where do you keep him?'

'Keep him?'

'I bet it's out there. Where the camp used to be. Some hovel near the great river, eh?'

'You're mad.' Yokabed walked on.

The woman wailed after her. 'Don't think it will be permitted. Don't think . . .'

That night Yokabed had Amram steal tar from the cooper's shed, where buckets and barrels were made. Next morning she took it to the shed. Miriam had slept the night there, listening to owls and field-mice, praying to the Old One in case vipers entered the place.

Now the two of them worked on the little ship. Yokabed the hull, Miriam the lid. They melted tar and sealed the cracks with it.

Before first light they left the shed, heading north-east. Close to the river they walked on the raised pathway connecting one irrigation ditch to another. They met peasants drawing water from the river for the millet fields. Soon they were amongst the workers of Princess Aniva-Hathi's estate.

Perhaps the peasants didn't often meet anyone to look down on, so they made jokes about the two Hapiru women. Yokabed carried the little ark on her hip, like a laundry-basket. No one troubled them about it.

By mid-morning they could see the Bubastis villa of Princess Aniva-Hathi

a mile down river. The rushes all about made it easy for them to crawl nearer along the bank. They heard noises amongst the stalks at the water's edge. River rats, or snakes. Bubastis was a snake-worship town, so it stood to reason snakes were plentiful in the area.

Yokabed and Miriam, with their package, lay close in to the villa. They could see the stone façade, the sculpted gods who kept it in place, the walled garden with pomegranate trees, and a pavement running down into the water. At noon a procession left the house. First saffron priests, then the princess in a tall, flat-topped hat, then women body-servants carrying towels and lotions. The priests fanned out either side of the pavement and faced the river.

A little behind them the princess disrobed. She had the blue and golden hat taken off, her belt undone. The dress that exposed one small breast was taken off, exposing another, and thin hips. The rings were pulled from her fingers. Naked, she wore her vast henna wig swept back over her ears. It seemed to dominate the little body. When it was removed, Miriam saw the head was shaved bald – in disgrace, or as an offering.

Miriam said, 'She will certainly need a wet nurse. To raise a fat baby.'

Aniva-Hathi's maids began to cover her with mud from the shallows. She took it without moving. She became a black princess. The priests chanted.

> *Lord of the river and of that quickening mud,*
> *Whence all manner of lowly things are brought to birth,*
> *Bring to thy servant the gift of fecundity,*
> *That she be not despised among the lowlier daughters of the earth,*
> *And the worth of her birth be matched by the worth of thy gift.*
> *Lift her, O river lord, to the ranks of the mothers.*

When the chant ended, the princess walked all muddied into the water and washed herself clean. A lonely stick of a girl, the priests and the maids staring at her from the bank. As she left the water, the priests went back to the villa. She robed on the bank and then was gone herself, back to a fitful afternoon nap.

Yokabed used the dry tips of bulrushes as a test. She floated them downstream all afternoon. An eddy seemed to sweep them all in to the princess's beach.

Dark. Prayers to the Old One. If he does not fetch up on the princess's beach, God of Abraham, let him be tangled in reeds in a place we can find him.

The biting damp of a night by the river. But the child is warm, inside Yokabed's dress. Dawn. A year-long morning.

There was a saffron movement in the doorway of the villa. 'Now?' Miriam asked. 'Not yet!' Yokabed told her.

People are always looking for symbols but sometimes life provides them free. As the mother and the daughter hovered, a terrible little corpse with a swollen belly sailed drunkenly downstream. What camp had it come from, to sail with Moses?

The moment they saw it, Yokabed said *yes*, as if inspired. She pushed the small boat through the screen of reeds into the water. And the live child and the dead floated in towards the bathing beach of Princess Aniva-Hathi. Darting amongst the rushes, Yokabed and Miriam kept abreast of the small boat. The princess had washed the mud from her eyes and body when she saw the little corpse. She screamed and jumped from the water. The priests lowered their eyes. She harangued them in a thin, jolting voice.

'You talk to the river as a river of life. It sends me a carrion baby? What does it mean? *What does it mean?*'

They didn't try to say.

'My Lady,' a maid said. She had seen the tiny ark of the baby about to beach itself. But at the last it hung off-shore, a little aloof, and the child in it began wailing.

The princess then saw it too. It meant the message from the river was not straightforward – 'Your womb is a grave,' for example – but more complicated.

'I must have it,' the princess said. 'You must get it, quickly.'

A half-naked negro servant picked the basket out of the water. She opened it and showed Aniva-Hathi what was inside. 'Healthy,' said the princess. With an effort she pulled the baby out, lifted its gown, felt its limbs. It kept slipping down her wet, frail body. 'Healthy,' she said. She showed one of its plump legs to her priests.

'Healthy!' she screamed.

From their place in the reeds, Yokabed and Miriam could tell the child had found a lofty home. They began crying secretly, not knowing what to think about it.

A Wet Nurse for the Lawgiver

It was a lax household. The ladies-in-waiting called the guards in from the river gate, and they too were asked to admire the child. Miriam was able herself to creep up to the river gate. 'Rings of fat,' she heard the lady say. 'Strong little feller,' a soldier told the princess.

One of the saffron priests had come back out of the house and looked calmly over the shoulders of the women.

'He must be somebody's child, Madame. You notice he is circumcised. That can only be done by human hand.'

All the ladies and the princess turned to him, a cat-like sneer on their faces.

'Whoever,' said Aniva-Hathi, 'is his mother, the river is his father. And has now given him to me.'

All the ladies clapped.

'If it makes Madame happy . . .' The priest turned away and walked back up the garden, shimmering like a pomegranate. All this Miriam was able to see from the river gate.

Now she stepped into the garden. She could feel the tender grass under her feet. Princess Aniva-Hathi was distressed because the baby was crying. She began to sing.

> *Out of the desert the wind blows strong,*
> *But cool from out of the sea;*
> *The desert burns and the day is long,*
> *but night sends my loved one back to me . . .*

When Aniva-Hathi stopped singing, her mouth was set in a permanent smile. Yet the baby was still crying.

Miriam said, 'He's hungry.'

They all looked towards her. Only the child went on making a noise. Miriam said, 'He only cries because he's hungry.'

It was easy for the ladies-in-waiting to decide what Miriam was. A Hapiru child dressed in sacking.

A maid asked one of the soldiers, 'Why don't you get rid of her?'

'No! Come over here!' Aniva-Hathi called to Miriam.

As Miriam walked up, she could smell perfume and river mud. For, beneath a linen overall her maids had slipped over her body, Aniva-Hathi was still smeared with Nile silt.

'How do you know he is hungry?'

'Madame, the hunger cry is different from every other cry.'

The skinny princess shivered. Maybe because Miriam, at eleven, had a sinister quality to her voice. It was to last her through life.

'Watch her closely,' Aniva-Hathi said quickly to her guards.

Now there are a lot of Nubians in the Egyptian army. Big fellows, frowners, the whites of their eyes of the purest white, their irises burning. On sentry duty, they carry copper battle axes. They march in an ominous, slow, rhythmic step which drill sergeants call the cadence step.

At the order from Aniva-Hathi, four guards formed up, thrust their battle axes before them, and marched to surround the Hapiru child. The baby still bawled and the princess made guttural crooning noises at it.

The copper axes didn't cure Miriam of her impudence. 'He needs a breast,' she called to the princess.

'Girl, answer me precisely. Do you know this child?'

'I am Hapiru, Ma'am. You know we have no baby boys. They are drowned, in wagon loads.'

'It must be necessary,' crooned Aniva-Hathi in the direction of the child's screaming face. Then she pounded her thigh with her thin fist. 'It must be necessary!' she called loudly.

The child still yelled for food. The princess made a pained face, closed her eyes. 'The child must be fed. Is there anyone at court who is in milk?'

None of the maids could answer. Opening her eyes, the princess grew a little peevish with Miriam. 'This child. Do you . . . do you know his mother?'

'Ma'am, I know good, clean Hapiru women. Their milk pains them. I could find Madame a Hapiru woman who would be happy to serve her.'

'How soon? How soon? After all, it is important.'

'Within an hour.'

'Then go, shoo!'

The eleven-year-old walked out from the encirclement of copper battle axes. At the gate, she turned and called across the garden. 'Madame.' Again the princess and the maids were interrupted in their frowning examination of the baby. 'Babies like him like a thumb dipped in honey.'

'Yes. Yes!' Aniva-Hathi agreed. 'I imagine they would. All the same you will hurry.'

In case there was anyone in the villa canny enough to suspect their stratagem, Miriam and Yokabed remained for a full hour hidden amongst reeds, listening to their son and brother howling for a nipple through the open galleries of the villa. He filled Aniva-Hathi's household with his complaint as easily as he had filled the brickworks shed.

'Poor little fellow,' said Yokabed. But if she walked in now, they might understand that it was maternity that moved her. 'Did you tell them about a thumb in honey?' Later she said, 'He'll get very dry crying like that.'

In the early afternoon they presented themselves to the big Nubians at the river gate. Miriam spoke up, Yokabed kept her head down. They were playing on the notorious Egyptian softness for children. They were led up the low terraces and around a fountain. They could not hear the baby. Had Aniva-Hathi found an alternative wet-nurse? They walked into a portico open to river breezes. In a long, high living-room, Aniva-Hathi tottered up and down with the baby, making soothing noises with her mouth. The child, face pink and swollen, had fallen asleep.

'You were so long!' she accused Miriam.

She pointed Yokabed to a cradle in the corner. Beside the cradle stood a chair. There Yokabed was to sit and feed the child.

When Yokabed was in position and had opened her dress, a Nubian girl washed her breasts with rosewater. Then the child was given to the Hapiru woman. Yokabed tried to receive him neutrally, without giving away her loss or her hunger. The baby boy didn't show any such inhibitions. He clamped on the nipple hard enough to make her grunt. Aniva-Hathi stood above them. She looked at Yokabed's breasts with some jealousy.

'Does your breast hurt?'

'A little, Ma'am.'

'Was your child . . . ?'

'My son is gone.'

'It's hard for women to understand any of it. Men are obsessed with politics and death. They build such complicated chambers and tunnels for both these purposes. We are a different race.'

And to herself she began to quote that famed Egyptian poem called *The Man Who Was Tired of Life*.

> *Death is in my sight today,*
> *As when a sick man becomes well again,*
> *Like going out of doors after detention . . .*

> *Death is in my sight today,*
> *Like the perfume of lotuses,*
> *Like sitting on the shore of the land of drunkenness . . .*

For a second there was a smell of sepulchres in the tall chamber.

'Yokabed tried to receive him neutrally,
without giving away her loss or her hunger'

'Hapiru woman, have you a husband?'

'Yes.'

'Where are you slaves?'

'At . . . at Pithom, Madame.' Yokabed flinched, waiting to be asked why are you so far from your work camp? Do you have permission? But the princess cared nothing for the little details of her father's State.

'You must live here now. There is a nursery you have to keep clean. You must rise to my son in the night. You will be happy if you make him happy.' She laughed for a second at the way the baby was guzzling. Her maids laughed too. 'Let me have your name.'

Yokabed gave it.

'I shan't forget it. Feed my son well.'

She began to move away towards her bathroom. Yokabed called after her. 'Ma'am. So I will know . . . what do you mean to call the child?'

'He must be called Meses. Like his grandfather. The prefix I shall think about. But Meses will do. Doesn't it mean, *given up to me by the river*?'

The maids clapped.

The royal party went out. In the large room there was one Nubian soldier, the baby prince, its wet-nurse, and Miriam.

'Will you be safe travelling back?' Yokabed asked her daughter.

'Of course, Yokabed mother.'

'If men stop you, pretend you're an idiot. They are superstitious about doing anything to idiots.'

'I know, I know.'

Their family conversation echoed off the tiling and they looked up shocked to see that Aniva-Hathi had come back and was in the doorway. She had had afterthoughts.

'Your husband,' she called. 'He may visit you here. But he may not stay. I will not have my son influenced by a Hapiru man.'

Yokabed was given a small pay. Each week she sent it home to Amram in Pithom camp by Miriam's hands. Perhaps Amram used some of it on palm wine from the commissariat, to console himself for loss of son and wife. Perhaps, in the palm wine, he talked. Anyhow, Miriam used to tell of travelling cross-country to Pithom, arriving with the cash in a handkerchief, and being hooted all the way down the main street.

'Her mother sold her baby brother to the Egyptians. Whores sell their babies. Whores!'

In the corner of the barracks, Aaron, about five years, knew he was suffering for a baby brother, and that mothers would not let their children play with him on account of that baby brother. Knew that Yokabed could not have him at the royal villa in case he gave the baby brother away. It's no wonder that there would always be some resentment there.

At the villa near Bubastis, the Pharaoh stopped by the cradle to inspect the child. Yokabed could tell he thought his daughter had come unhinged. He looked knowingly at Yokabed for a second. She dropped her eyes. Any second, she thought, He'll say *Own up, it's a little Hapiru, isn't it, escaped from the dragnet?* He knew the river did not give up babies to skinny princesses. Yet Aniva-Hathi felt justified now, for the royal clothes she wore, the royal food she ate. He would not destroy that for her. He did not invite her back from Bubastis, but he let her keep the baby.

At last even the princess's husband, a diplomat who had been away in Assyria, visited Aniva-Hathi. He cringed at everything about his wife, her turns of phrase, her dithery excitement over the baby. 'If it makes you

happy, dear,' he kept saying over and over. He did not even stay overnight.

Aniva-Hathi began to become jealous of Yokabed. It was as simple as this; she envied her her plentiful lap and breasts. Sometimes she would come into the nursery toward the end of the child's feeding and say, 'When he has finished breast feeding, he'll be totally mine. You will forget him. He will forget you. When they ask him who his mother is, he'll give my name.'

Yokabed kept her eyes down. One word of cheek, she suspected, and she was out. 'That's only as it should be, Ma'am,' she would say.

By being biddable and cunning, she was able to stay on till the boy was seven. Then she was sent packing back to Pithom, where she and Amram were to die in their corner of the barracks.

Before she left, the child gave her an obsidian snake. He knew that in the religion of the Israeli Hapirus, snakes indicated demons. He was the sort of little boy who thought that the best thing you could do for adults was give them a pleasant fright. 'Maybe it will keep you safe from adders, nanny Yokabed,' he told her.

Her going wasn't easy for him either. From now on he would share his quarters with a priest and a tutor. Experts would come in and teach him the use of weapons. He would be expected to learn a headful of hieroglyphic symbols, and to observe and pick up hints from the dissection of the dead.

Yokabed found her way home through the stands of sedge and papyrus. She would never see *child* Moses again.

The Lawgiver's Education

Now the Moses I knew had certainly been brought up in an expensive Egyptian household. He told me that at one stage he had daily elocution lessons for his speech defect. They had only done a little good. He also commented that Egyptians thought it bad for a prince to have few sexual outlets. Royal officials selected and primed girls, introducing them into the prince's garden or apartments, where he came across them like gifts left by visitors.

Anyhow, Miriam always said Aniva-Hathi's household was the one in which her brother was installed. Twenty years later, Miriam met an Egyptian official called Moses or Meses, who said he was Aniva-Hathi's son. When Miriam told him, you are my brother, he never denied it. Perhaps he was being polite. Perhaps he was showing political sense. It would be hard for him to control the Israeli Hapiru if he were not believed to be one of them.

Also, the Israelis used words like sister, brother, wildly, as symbols.

Just the same, I have to admit: The boy who arrived on Aniva-Hathi's beach was probably the Moses who led the clans out into the waterless wastes. Mad things happen in this world.

This next bit I know from conversations with Moses in the wilderness south of Kadesh.

Aniva-Hathi never mentioned anything about the river giving him to her. Yet he could always tell there was something strange about his birth. It was clear to him that he could never succeed to the Pharaoh's throne. Whenever he asked her why, Aniva-Hathi had hysterics. It was only when he met Miriam that he got some sort of explanation for all this.

He loved the princess very much. She had always had a weak chest, and grew tubercular towards the end of his boyhood. The good climate kept her going, rather short of breath. Towards the end of her life, she often wanted him to sit with her all night. She gave him amethysts and carbuncles to pass on to the girls he would normally have spent his night with.

'You are a good boy. You give them up without complaint. I can smell the young flesh and the desire,' she would say, as if the girls were there in her big sterile bedroom. 'Beyond the west, perhaps I will have young flesh. Perhaps I will be a girl, waiting for a boy. He needn't bring amethysts.'

'The bandaging did not start till after the seventieth day'

OVERLEAF 'The body was moved up-river to Pi-Rameses, to the royal embalming shop there'

One of the girls, accepting his jewel, looked peevish. 'What use are you to her? You can't make her breathe more easily. Me, however . . .'

He had *that* girl taken away. Whenever she tried to come back to his apartments, copper axes were crossed to bar her way.

What sort of student was he? He was adequate at anatomy. He was good at making verses. Because it was a country house and he would never spend much time at court, the priests and tutors taught the things he would not have learned closer to the Pharaoh. The story, for example, of the Pharaoh Akhnaton, who banned all the animal gods of Egypt and worshipped only the one pure God, the Aton, whose symbol was the sun. Of how all this ran counter to the interests of the priests of Amon, whose temples were centres of political and financial influence. Of how these priests poisoned Akhnaton and his statuesque wife, Nefertiti. Of how then, they bullied Tutankhaton, Akhnaton's step-son, into changing his name to Tutankhamon, in honour of their own fat god, and then with their knowledge of physics, poisoned him before he turned twenty.

He learnt good medicine. The Egyptians are the best doctors in the world. When you go into the desert and wander with Israelis you forsake the good medicine of Egypt. Moses used often to speak to Aniva-Hathi about her condition.

'There are ways that lead to your lungs. They are mere piping. The lungs themselves are mere bellows. If men can clear a blocked duct, if they can repair a bellows, why can't they make you breathe?'

'The next time,' Aniva-Hathi said, 'anyone attends to my organs, it will be to take them out of me for burial, to place them reverently in jars.'

Moses hushed her. 'But I am content.' she told him. 'I will go westward on a boat, the way the sun goes. The sun absorbs us all, you know. I shouldn't say it. It is greater than the river. My grave is over.there, in the sun's direction, under the sandstone cliffs. I will embark on a boat whose pennant is: The sun that shines in the night. Whose name is the name of the god of the harvest of the souls. Whose oars are the arms of a god whose face we must not see. Beyond the west bank, I will find a secret way into the earth.'

The night Aniva-Hathi died, Moses was due to leave Bubastis on an inspection of the new delta grain-cities. He postponed it. The body was moved up river to Pi-Rameses, to the royal embalming shop there. Here it was gutted and dried with soda and resins for more than two months. The bandaging did not start till after the seventieth day. Moses knew all about the process from his education. How many layers of bandages, what preservatives they were dipped in, how the liver and lungs, the intestines and the

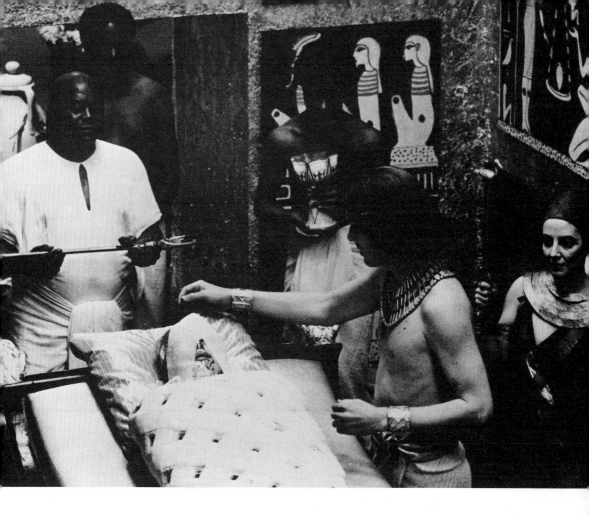

stomach were put into sealed jars. On each of the four jars the head of one of the four sons of Horus. In this long drawn way, the Egyptians sucked on death like a child on candy.

On the proper day, Moses was in Pi-Rameses to ride up river with his mother's body. It disgusted him, the number of dancers and mourners the Pharaoh had employed to fall about and wail for this neglected daughter of the royal house.

The coffin was dragged by oxen to its well-designed grave in the sandstone. Egyptian tombs are terrible places. Slaves with torches go ahead of you. The Sem-priest, wearing black, walks by the body. You feel that an accident of draught will blow all the lights out. That you'll be left blinking, blind, lost in this sophisticated hole in the earth.

The mummy is put against a wall. The Sem-priest prances up to it with little knives of obsidian. He makes motions on the outer carton, which is in the likeness of the dead person, as if he intends to prise the corpse's eyes open. Then the lips. Then ears, and so on.

He intones such things as: 'Your lips I open in the god's name, that you

may speak and eat. Your eyes I open in the god's name, that light and sight may bless them.'

Some tart of a priestess minces up and pretends to be the soul of the dead person, begging for pardon for its little or big meannesses during this life.

'Now I am nothing, let my crimes be as nothing. Now that I am beyond the river, let my sins be as passing sunlight on the river. You who are the great unnamed god of the underworld, I want but to see your face, to sing your songs. And to see the faces and sign the names of the hundred sweet gods who eat at your table.'

Choking, Moses saw furniture brought in. Aniva-Hathi would need it in the world to which she had gone. Inlaid seats, it seemed, and vintage wine. Corn cakes. Roast lamb. The mummy was lowered into its cavity. From urns carried round by servants, Pharaoh Rameses, his ten-year-old son Mernefta, the queen – a fat Hittite woman – all scooped up and sprinkled dust on their own heads and shoulders in a bored sort of manner. Servants carried in the Answerers, little pottery figures who were packed into a box in the funeral chamber. The priest intoned, 'When dear Aniva-Hathi is called on in the afterlife to perform any arduous or forced labour, to plough fields or build dams, to haul stone or carry sand, you shall all answer *I will do it, here I am.*'

After the funeral, Rameses touched his putative grandson on the elbow.

'You ought to keep busy now, son. You were to go to Pi-Rameses?'

'Yes, sir.'

'That was only a training trip, to let you see what to look for. But you're a bright boy. You don't need to be told these things. I want you to go to Pithom. It's a slack camp. We've never had a first-class commissioner there. After thirty years, the grain city of Pithom isn't quite finished. Look around. Stir up the commissioners. Above all, I want a report. Something to take action on.'

'Very well.'

'You know, my daughter Aniva-Hathi, poor woman – she would have had a dreadful life without you.'

When Moses went south to Pithom, wearing a simple white tunic and riding a white horse, he carried documents with Pharaoh's seal on them. He felt sober. This is where my career starts he thought. Since it had looked once that he'd never have a career, he felt grateful now.

An official from the Office of Works rode with him.

'Do you ever have much trouble from these Hapiru?' he asked the man.

'No. They're amenable. As you'll see, sir.'

Pithom was what Rameses called a granary city. Its skyline was a series of great pot-bellied silos. In Pithom were all the officials and private businesses connected with the storing and distribution of wheat and millet. Builders, furnishers, most trades, all sorts of craft shops found good business in such towns. They rented their premises from the government.

For a little time the road to Pithom ran along the caravan route to Arabia. 'North of the road is Pithom city,' one of his escort told him. 'South is the labour camp.'

'I shall have to go and see the labour camp.'

He had never been to workings before. He was very interested to see how the great stones were lifted and levered. But they entered the city and he was bathing in the commissioner's house before he had a chance to see any great convoy of stones coming down the road.

The commissioner was a fat, genial man with a pencil-thin moustache. He was aware that there was some official disapproval of the rate of work in Pithom. He and his wife were therefore nervous of Moses.

In the evening they stood together in the foyer and welcomed guests to a dinner in honour of Moses. Pots of vintage wine and casks of beer stood in the central dining-room. The menu was fish, roast duck, roast beef. After his sheltered life in the household of Aniva-Hathi, the fuss these people made of him, the way they held their breath waiting for his opinions, turned his head a little. Very thirsty from his journey to Pithom, he drank large amounts of beer. The commissioner had depended on it. You can always depend on a favour, or at least less harshness, from someone you've made drunk. Like a loser, he got drunk himself.

Moses kept waving to one of the girls in the floor show.

'It can be arranged,' the commissioner muttered at him.

'Not that blind harper. Not him. I mean the dancer.'

'I know you mean the dancer. No one's much interested in blind harpers.' And they giggled fraternally.

Later in the evening Moses was aware of lurching round the garden with his host. The commissioner was opening his heart to the young official. As he spoke he patted a pet cat he carried in his arms, hugging it pretty heavily. Moses could hear it hissing in the man's grasp. 'The slackness goes all down the line,' said the commissioner. 'Assistant commissioners, superintendents, overseers, foremen.'

'Do your foremen use the lash much?'

'Yes. But they'll use it more. You can leave it to me. I'll see they use it more.'

Moses understood, in that garden while drunk, that he felt no passion for Pharaoh's troubles in Pithom. He had no gift for playing the grand bureaucrat. He'd grown up in a quiet house in the country, had always been treated

as some sort of bastard. Now he found he didn't wish to spend his life travelling round the marvellous work-sites, making hell for poor incompetents like this one.

'I have to confess, sir. I have to confess that I'm a little soft on them myself. You see . . . I respect them.'

'You respect them? The Hapiru?'

'Well they have a certain pride. They call *us* the uncircumcised.'

'Us?' Moses still remembered the mass circumcision ceremony in the Temple of Horus at Bubastis on a summer's night when he was fourteen. Sixty boys had been circumcised in the one ceremony. The priests told each boy that he was neither to hit out or be hit, neither to scratch or to be scratched. In other words, lie still and grit your teeth. 'Don't they know we also practise circumcision?'

'Yes. But they still call us the *uncircumcised*. And they have this god. Now they are not meant to name his name but it is el Shaddai. There is no image for this god. Not the sun, not a crow or a heifer or a crocodile. You've got to admit, that's pretty remarkable. Have you ever met people with one god and there's no image for him? In a way it makes sense. Do you really believe there are gods shaped like this?'

And, too brutally, he raked his cat's ears back and presented its face to Moses. The cat sprang from his arms and raked its claws across Moses' cheek. It ran away into the dark.

'Oh,' said the commissioner. 'Oh.'

Moses was annoyed. 'We'll talk tomorrow. You mentioned that dancer.'

'I thought it would be all right. But she said she had to go.'

'How can you build a store city when you cannot even arrange for a dancer?'

Even as he marched away, he grew sorry for the man, who would go back to his bedroom and weep at his wife's side.

The Lawgiver commits a Murder

T he next bit I have from Miriam. Once more — if what she says is right, then the child she floated on the river became the Moses I met in the desert.

The Hapirus of Pithom labour camp knew, during the next few days, that they and their overseers were being inspected. The official was a young man wearing the blue-and-gold top hat of someone important. Sometimes he would ride through their camp alone, talking to individual slaves as if he was interested in them for purposes of study. When he'd ride on, they'd make jokes about the way he spoke.

He stopped all the old men. 'I believe you have a god called el Shaddai?'

'Well . . . yes, your honour.'

'That there is no image for el Shaddai?'

'And his name, sir. His *real* name. El Shaddai isn't it. It's a cover up name.'

This much he got slowly from the old men. They didn't want to tell him. 'Isn't there someone who would discuss el Shaddai with me?'

'I can't think of one, sir.'

'Does el Shaddai want to go on being just the god of Pithom labour camp?'

'I don't know what his plans are, sir.'

Late on the afternoon of the third day of his visit, riding alone, he passed the door of some sort of storage shed on the edge of the workings. From inside the shed came all the noises of a beating up. He got down from his horse and walked inside.

Two Israeli slaves stood holding a third slave fast with ropes around his wrists. An Egyptian overseer was flogging the man. Sometimes he used the thongs of the lash, sometimes its weighted leather handle.

'Sir,' one of the Israeli slaves called to the overseer. The overseer paused, turned, saw Moses, smiled, bowed deeply, and turned back to his discipline.

'Explain yourself!' Moses called across the earth floor. Because of his impediment, the overseer pretended not to hear. 'Explain yourself!' he repeated.

The overseer bowed exactly as he had when Moses first arrived. Then he said, 'I am punishing the man because he attacked me.'

The overseer had a square and nearly honest peasant face. Moses would have reason to remember it. The tied Israeli grunted and made his accusation. 'He was with my wife. She did not want him to have her.'

The two Israelis against the wall began squinting and quivering. They thought their friend tied to the wheel was being insolent. 'An overseer,' one of them said, 'has to have some rights. He works hard. These things happen. The woman's very good to look at. Very, very good.'

The man on the wheel yelled, 'Damn you. Damn you for tying me up. Damn you for your knots.'

The Israelis against the wall grew hurt and angry. 'Damn you,' they screamed. 'Damn you. You'd knot us up, you trusty bastard.'

The man on the wheel began weeping. 'El Shaddai, el Shaddai.'

Moses was already so taken with the idea of el Shaddai that he called, 'Stop!' The overseer would not stop. 'Stop!' Could it be my impediment? he asked himself. Or is the man deaf?

Prince Moses went up to him and touched his shoulder. The man shrugged his hand off. Next Moses put his hand firmly on the shoulder. The man swatted it across the knuckles. 'You do this?' Moses screamed, meaning, you do this to an Egyptian prince? And though he was angry, he thought this overseer is now locked up in the role of flogger and can never again be

'The overseer turned, walked away as if he
had lost interest in beating up Hapiru,
then fell on the dirt floor'

reached. He is like a crocodile locked into a pattern of attack. He has to be stopped.

Prince Moses took a shovel from the floor. He hit the overseer with the flat of the blade where the man's neck met his shoulder. The overseer turned, walked away as if he had lost interest in beating up Hapiru, then fell on the dirt floor. His eyes were open, and there was no movement in the V of chest Moses could see.

'El Shaddai,' he accused the Israelis. 'El Shaddai, your god, made him deaf. El Shaddai. Your god.'

Moses straddled the man's chest and beat at his dead chaps. 'Not our god, sir. And you can believe us, we won't gossip.'

'I've killed an Egyptian,' said Prince Moses. He knew what it meant. He was Rameses least favourite grandson. The Pharaoh would spare him a trial but expect him to suicide ritually. He would be forced to sit in a hot bath and open the veins in his elbows. The two Israelis were trying to cut down their friend without being seen. They wanted to remove all Hapiru evidence from the place of the crime.

'Run, run,' Moses said. 'But keep it secret. Secret, do you understand? Only in your silences, tell el Shaddai that he made the man deaf.'

He rode back to the commissioner's house. The commissioner was sitting meekly there, his jaw in his hand, waiting for him. 'Your honour, I have decided that I must resign. I have a small villa to retire to. I am very sad to have proved inadequate . . .'

'No, no, no,' Prince Moses said absently. 'You ought to stay . . .'

He was thinking of one thing only: Was it or was it not wise to leave Pithom straight away. He decided that the next afternoon he would put on a simple white tunic and go walking in the camp. If any of the three men had gossiped about the death, it would be news throughout Pithom and he would overhear.

He lay on his bed and wept. 'Oh, brother, oh, brother,' he said. He thought of that not quite honest, not quite clever overseer face confused and blinking in the strange dark land of the dead. When the body was found, he would see a priest and set up a temple trust fund so that a year's supply of bread and beer could be bought to keep the overseer going in the land of death.

He barely slept that night. There was a flavour of dirt in his mouth.

The commissioner interrupted his breakfast. 'Sir, we now have a pretext. We can crack down, so to speak. An Egyptian overseer has been killed. Fracture of the brain. Hit from behind with a shovel.'

Wearily, and to his own surprise, Moses spoke up. 'It wasn't them. It was me.'

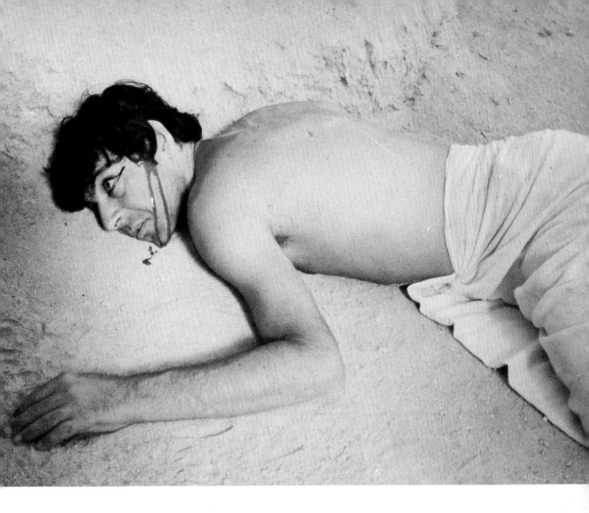

'That's not possible.'

But Moses explained it.

The commissioner thought a second.

'You come in here, threatening me, threatening my position, robbing me of sleep, and it turns out you're a brawler.'

Moses still felt oddly detached. 'If it was a brawl, it was a strange sort of brawl.'

'I will have you arrested straight away.'

'No. You wouldn't know if that was right. A grandson of Rameses. It's a risk to arrest a grandson of Rameses. For anything.'

The man bunched his face like a fist. 'I shall report this. I shall report it and say it over and over again. Otherwise you will destroy me. You will have me assassinated in my villa. I will say it and say it.'

'You're safe. You're safe.'

'Get out.'

Prince Moses went to the stables and called for his horse. He thought, I can deny it, that I ever spoke those things to the commissioner. It will have to be

that way. The Hapiru are responsible for the death. El Shaddai made the man
deaf. I must first find out if the Hapiru are talking.

In a plain white suit he rode into Pithom camp. Even cities in that part of
the world can be cluttered. There are no straight alleys, no organised passage
ways. It is like being in a forest. So it would have been lean and crooked
alley ways that Prince Moses rode down alone. On the edge of a clear space
somewhere in the camp, he saw a crowd. They were watching two Hapiru
men beat each other up. There was cheering, and laughter when blows were
missed or unexpectedly landed. He didn't know why he called out – perhaps
it was the habit of commanding slaves in the villa near Bubastis. But he called
out. He told them to stop.

Only the spectators separated them. They were both spitting mad. One of
them gestured with his free fist in the Egyptian's direction.

'The Prince Moses. Are you going to be our judge? Are you going to
murder us? Like you murdered the Egyptian?'

All the crowd looked wide-eyed. They lowered their eyebrows and looked
under them, more or less fearfully, at Moses. He could tell they all knew.

He wanted to get out of the whole knowing camp.

Risking a fall, he shook his horse's reins and put the spurs in. Unsure of his
direction, he was aware of a woman running behind him. Over his shoulder,
he got jolting glimpses of her. About thirty, long legged, a little craggy, her
skirts pulled up to the knees to allow her to run. In the crooked streets, in
fact, she could run as fast as he could ride. What is her purpose? he wondered. At a corner his horse's forefoot slewed in a sewer. He felt the animal
going down, got his feet from the stirrups and jumped free, not without
hitting himself about on the mud-brick corner.

When he was clear-headed again, the Hapiru woman was beside him. She
was smoothing his hair, an amazing presumption.

'My Lord,' she said. 'My mother was your nurse in Bubastis.'

'Your mother?'

'Yokabed. You were too young when she left to understand where she
was going. *This* was where she was going.'

He said, 'Hapiru woman, can you help me?'

'Come on. My brother will hide your horse.'

Amram's family had by now moved out of their corner of the barracks and,
as slaves of long standing and good character, been given a little place of
their own, a three-walled brick shed, curtained off on the side facing the
alley. They had the luxury of an outside staircase, so that they could sleep on
the roof on hot nights. The whole place was six paces by ten.

Inside stood two old people. The curtains that made the fourth wall were

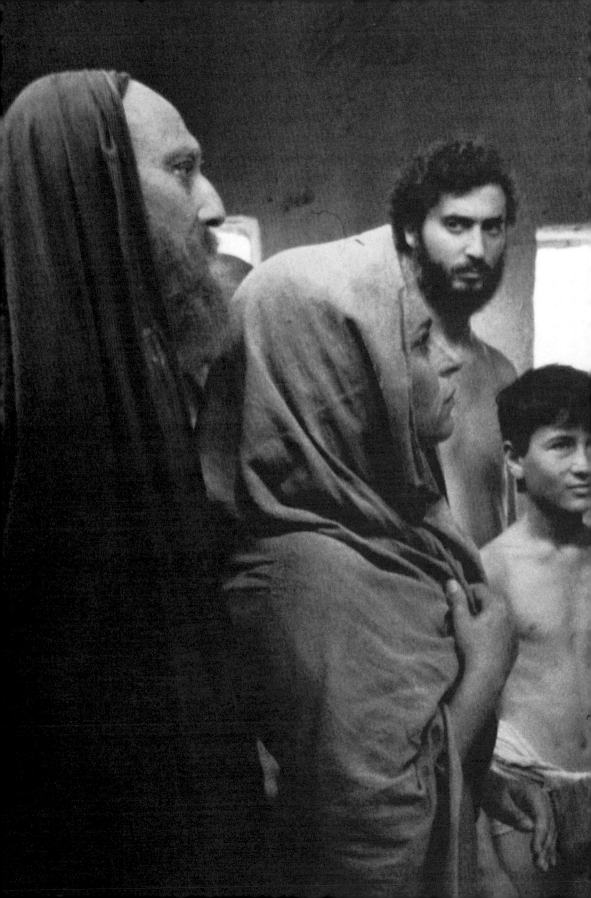

down, so that it was hard to see them. Prince Moses peered at the woman, trying to remember what he could of Yokabed, his nurse. All he recalled was a certain fullness of the face; it had been a sweet face with a good mouth. There wasn't much fullness of face any more in this old woman who rose and stared at him.

'Do you remember me?' She used no titles.

'If you're Yokabed, I remember Yokabed.' The old woman was trembling and the old man circling the visitor, giggling a little.

'Let me tell you this. When you were six you had measles. You were rest-less in the nursery. Your moth . . . the *princess* . . . she brought you a wooden tiger so high. It had wheels attached to its paws. I used to haul you round the nursery on it.'

'There are many such toys in the kingdom of Egypt.'

'You called yours Sali. You were a great one for secret names and you would only let the princess and myself know that one. Do you want to know more? On your wall there's a painting of a little boy, wearing the sun on his head, going fowling with a bow and a stick amongst the papyrus reeds. His cat was dragging the fowls down out of the air.'

She had made his childhood immediate to him again. He put a hand on her shoulder. 'Yokabed,' he said happily. The greeting was all the more hearty because those nursery days were a sunny escape from a certain poisonous reality: That he was a royal murderer and would be asked to bleed himself to death.

Yokabed hugged him. 'Lord, Lord,' she said.

Miriam broke this up. 'That's not how it is. First I must send for my brother Aaron. Wait here with my parents.'

By this time Miriam had no doubt that the prince was her brother. There-fore she went to the gate of the brickworks. On great trays set in the sun Hapiru slaves packed clay and straw into brick moulds. Here Aaron worked under an Israeli foreman. Miriam went in and told the foreman Aaron's mother was very sick. Aaron was grudgingly released.

Aaron, even grown up, had a margin of resentment for his brother. His mother had left him at the age of five to go and wet-nurse the child. Amram and Aaron used to trail into the villa occasionally on visits. When Aniva-Hathi sacked Yokabed, Aaron was thirteen. For the rest of his boyhood he had to listen to Yokabed reminiscing about life with *that* child in the nursery at Bubastis. Aaron thought it was unlucky that he had no place either in his mother's obsessions or in the luxuries of the royal villa.

When they arrived home again, they found Yokabed and Amram still bowing and talking respectfully to Prince Moses. Aaron was amazed to see

his sister walk up to the man and hug him strenuously. He decided to remind them all of realities.

'What are you going to do?' he asked the Egyptian prince. 'You're certainly in trouble. The commissioner of Pithom rode off west in a flurry this afternoon. I suppose he's got something to report.'

'He has,' said Moses.

'That a Hapiru slave murdered an overseer?'

'That the grandson of Pharaoh murdered an overseer. Though murdered isn't exact . . .' Moses squinted at the floor. 'I know this, I would swear to it. That el Shaddai blocked the man's ears.'

'El Shaddai?'

'Blocked his ears, so he could not hear me order him to stop.'

Aaron said, 'It isn't normal for Egyptians to talk about el Shaddai.'

'One of the Israelis present called out for el Shaddai. Is it unlikely? Doesn't el Shaddai ever cut off people's hearing?'

Old Amram said, 'Sometimes he does.'

'I will have to go away,' said Prince Moses. 'I will need at least two asses. I will need heavy, ample clothes. I will need dried fruit and dried meat. Can you help me?'

'There's something you must know,' Miriam told the prince.

'Yes,' Amram announced, in a chanting voice.

'El Shaddai is our sun, our eagle, our sacred mountain and yours. El Elohe Yisrael is the only god and our god. He has chosen us.'

'Chosen?' The idea reverberated like a crack at the base of the skull.

'You mean, chosen you?'

'Chosen *us*!' Aaron said virulently.

'What sort of choosing? The way a businessman chooses a horse? The way a hunter chooses a dog? The way a boy chooses a girl? What sort of choosing?'

'Take your pick,' said Aaron.

'The way a boy chooses a girl,' said Yokabed.

'*Chosen!*' Moses said. 'The great gods of Egypt – and they were great gods – never chose anyone. They operate on their own plane.'

'What do you think of that?' Aaron challenged him.

Moses lost his temper. 'I would say that a god is very hard up to have to choose a scabby oaf like you.'

'You deserve that,' Miriam told Aaron.

'What did he *choose* you for?' Moses asked Amram. 'Your race.'

'To be his only people.'

'The only people of the only god?'

'Exactly. We have an arrangement with him. He intends to give us our own land.'

Amram closed his eyes and smiled. He had no reason for smiling. In his dark closet, by a sewer, under the skies of slavery.

Yokabed said, 'El Shaddai has chosen you, Prince Moses.'

Aaron grunted and shook his head.

'There's something they'll never get round to telling you,' Miriam called out. 'I have to do everything in this house. Now I have to do this. You, called Prince Moses, I want you to look at this your brother, Aaron. This sister, Miriam. And Yokabed, the woman who gave birth to you. And Amram, who sired you.'

'*What?*'

'It must be a surprise. Sit down and listen.'

Naturally Moses was full of the great yawning terror that comes with discovery. 'I don't want to hear.'

'Sit down,' Miriam ordered him.

And when he had heard it, his reaction was unexpected. When he couldn't understand it. It seemed the most natural thing to see these four as kin. It was as if, just beneath the surface of his mind, he had always suspected it. Just the same, he must have gone on being shocked.

After they'd all sat still for a while, Aaron spoke up. He didn't sound vindictive any more, only sad. 'We had this mad dream. One day, when you were a man of influence, we'd go to you and say, look at the way the government's treating your people. Now that you're under a shadow, you need *our* help, and your help is worth nothing to us.'

The Lawgiver escapes into the Sinai Desert

He stayed there three days. He was full of a mad elation at finding he was a slave's child. He also talked to Amram about the ritual and the lore of the tribe. Since he considered himself a scholar in these matters, it was all heady stuff to him.

He was beginning to think, three Israeli witnesses are nothing. Rameses will discount them. He'll remove the commissioner, who deserves to be removed anyhow. Then I can go back to Bubastis.

Reasonably enough, he was in two minds about everything.

On the third day, the commissioner rode back to Pithom. He had a dozen royal officers with him. A guard's officer, called Reteveh, walked through Pithom dressed in ordinary clothes. By bullying and cleverness he came to the door of Amram's place in the early evening. In he went without invitation. Prince Moses was there, sitting on the floor with the others, eating a mutton stew.

'Sit still,' said Reteveh. 'I am a lieutenant in the Guards. I must tell you, my Lord, that there is a warrant issued for your arrest.'

'On . . . on the word of three Israelis?'

'On the word of the Egyptian witnesses, too.'

'But there were no Egyptian witnesses.'

'The commissioner produced two. They were believed. He himself argued like a man fighting for his life. All that concerns you is this. The Pharaoh considers you have disgraced yourself. If you come home, you will be asked to put an end to yourself. Since he does not wish to execute the warrant against you in any way, he says you must go away towards Arabia for the rest of his life. At the ferry at Lake Timsah, a guide will be waiting for you. He will have money for you and a receipt which you must sign. He will have horses. Later he will acquire camels. He will take you across Sinai. You have to go immediately. Tomorrow the camp will be searched. Pharaoh feels bound to show, even people like this, that his warrants mean something. Goodnight.'

Prince Moses decided to travel immediately by moonlight. It is about twenty miles from Pithom to the Lake Timsah ferry, and he couldn't wait to get there. He wanted to find out if the supposed guide with money and horses was in fact a royal assassin, paid by the government to rid the country of certain vexatious people.

Yokabed moaned and sang a song about gaining a son and losing him, and gaining him again and losing him. Amram, whom Moses suspected of being a little senile, put his hands on the fugitive's head and blessed him with a long tribal blessing. During it he called el Shaddai, variously, the rock, the shepherd, the fortress, the shelter, the sun, the father, the mother-bird, the help, the shade, the portion, the song, the potter, the husband, the fountain, the dew, the lion. All these vivid terms lodged in the brain of the prince.

Miriam, the craggy lady, hugged him ferociously, looking into his eyes. 'I planned that you'd be a prince. I have loved you in your absence. We expect to see you again. Don't let us down.'

To travel by night in an ordered country like Egypt is very pleasing. Amongst the noise of owls and the industrious shufflings of mice. I once saw a lion quietly cross the road ahead of me. You get the impression that under that large moon no creature is at enmity with any other.

Aaron travelled a little way with Moses, turning back at midnight so that he'd be in time for work. Before he went, he talked a little self-consciously with Prince Moses.

'You'll have to forgive me for speaking to you so roughly. It's your mother and Miriam who do that to me. They're terrible women.'

'I begin to see that,' said Moses, remembering Miriam's goodbye.

'It's the truth, you know. All they say. I've been envying you since I was five.'

Moses smiled broadly. 'Now I can envy you.'

'Do you have a knife?'

'Yes.'

'Those women are convinced you can do anything.' Unsure of himself, he put his arm inside Moses' and grasped the bicep, squeezing it hard. 'All I say is, come back again.'

A moment's annoyance swept through Moses. Who do they think they are, making such demands?

By mid-morning he'd ridden down through stands of papyrus reeds to the Timsah ferry. Along the shore stood a litter of fishermen's huts, meaner than Amram's. There were three smelly hotels for businessmen crossing out of the Wilderness of Shur. Perhaps to someone coming out of the desert, they might look adequate.

Two ferrymen stood talking together in the shallows.

'If a man,' called Moses, 'were waiting for another man on important business in this place, where would he spend his time?'

Both ferrymen looked at him as if they knew exactly what he was talking about. 'I think you'll find the man you wish to meet at the Turnface.'

'Turnface?'

'The hotel. The big one.'

In the central courtyard of the inn of that unhappy name, Moses sat down to a cup of beer. The tables were pushed up hard against the south wall for the sake of shade. There were only two Egyptians talking business with two Arabs and the hotelier's daughter serving the strong ales of the Nile. Moses watched them all carefully. He thought, if they get up and go, I will get up and go too. I will not be left alone in a deserted courtyard.

The innkeeper came into the yard with a freshly hunted gazelle slung over his shoulders. He dumped it temporarily in a cool corner and came up smiling to Moses.

'Are you the Prince?' he muttered, still smiling. 'Yes you are. They showed me a brooch your mother had made.' He sat down. 'What was the name of the man who sent you here?'

Moses told him. Reteveh.

'What did he say you would be given?'

'Money.'

'Sign this receipt.'

Moses did so.

'It's a good amount,' said the hotelier. 'I wouldn't mind falling into disgrace if that's the amount they give you. However, it's not always much use out there.' He gestured eastwards.

'He mentioned horses. And a guide.'

'You will have two asses. One to ride, the other to carry a little army tent and waterbags. That's all. A guide is impossible. He'll come back and say that the Pharaoh's law is corrupt. Anyhow, it's all easy going. There are wells all the way south as far as the road junction. You go to the left there. The right leads to the mines. You will have to go about eighty or ninety miles without water, till you get to Nakhl. Then Themed. It won't be too bad.'

'And I just go now? Like that?'

'Yes. If you're not gone on this afternoon's ferry, the local authorities will jump on you.' The man got up and went to fetch his gazelle. Before he was there he remembered something, and returned to Moses.

'There is something I was strictly ordered to tell you. If nothing is heard of you, the produce of three fields will eventually be devoted to your upkeep in the land of the dead. This arrangement will operate in ten years' time, so don't die before that.'

The promise didn't interest Moses. Even though, less than a week before, he had tried to make arrangements for bread and beer for the Egyptian overseer.

So he vanished into the terrible land of Sinai, where there are no rivers.

It is brown country. Some scrub and tamarisk grow there. Some acacia shrubs. Thornbushes. It's arrogant of them to try. But it is a simple landscape, made up of sun and rock. Not that the nights aren't cold.

Two separate groups of Amalekite nomads forced him to ransom himself with large sums. Sometimes he travelled with other, more genial desert people. From them he learned how to prepare the desert food, what sort of porous rocks hold water, how to travel by fixing your eye on a star.

At the oasis of Nakhl he spent two months with the Bedouin, getting over a scorpion sting and then over the strange fever that followed. The Bedouin chief leant over Moses' pallet often and said, 'It is a rare sickness, this sickness that follows a scorpion sting. Most men get better in the space of a day, two perhaps. You are unlucky, dear man.'

It's because I'm confused, thought Moses. He had begun, a little guilty, a little resentful, to think of el Shaddai. Egypt was a land cluttered with features: River, groves, sedges, the western heights to which the dead travelled, the plush grasslands, the plentiful animals. There the sun was dominant and kind. It was easy to see behind each of these features a different god, with the face of an animal or the face of the sun. In Sinai there was only the sun and scorpions ravaging a corpse of a landscape. If the sun was a god here, it was an evil god. And no tribe worshipped the scorpion. At noon in that vacant country, when you were thirsty, you could feel a presence. A big presence. What was its face like? Like the poisonous scorpion? Like the murderous sun?

He thought, this is why the Hapiru, coming out of the desert, *knew* that there was no possible image for el Shaddai.

The chief gave him a girl, but he made a surly lover. Eventually he rode on to Themed, a miserable little village of mud brick houses high up on the plateau they called the Wilderness of Paran. If he had not had Bedouin friends, he would have been knifed in some miserable township such as Themed. For even though he had been months in the wilderness, he still had – by the standards of the desert – an expensive look.

Three weeks he spent in Themed. He was listless, and had a weird feeling he couldn't afford ever to leave town, to face the desert which he already thought of as el Shaddai's. Now I know it's quite normal for the desert to

upset people and jumble their nerves. But, having grown up in Bubastis,
Moses didn't.

So he lay on his bed a lot.

His Bedouin friends enjoyed Themed for seven days, but then wanted to
be off towards Elath and the Gulf of Aqabah and the nice pastures of Midian
beyond the Gulf. But he delayed them.

He felt better again as soon as they took to the road. From a bare, brown
hill beyond Elath he looked down into a valley where small shrubs grew.
As far as the Bedouins were concerned, this was good pasture.

One of them said, 'There is a town over there.'

This was where Moses was to meet his woman.

Down in that valley the Bedouin pitched their black, goats' hair tents.
Moses sat in the tent Pharaoh had appointed to him. He had the flaps back
and looked out at the red mountains of Arabia. In the late afternoon, some
Midian girls came through the shrubs, making for a well a little to the south.
They were dark, plump girls, Moses could see that. They drove sheep.
'Shepherdesses,' he said to himself.

He thought, what an amazing part of the world this is, all these little tribes, half settled, half wandering, undecided. A little scabby. But they all think they are *the* tribe, *the* people. So there is pride. And the women? He liked the look of them.

Now, amongst the Bedouin, women aren't heard of much. They keep their place. They don't have much character of their own. The men don't prize them much even as bed partners. So Moses felt elated to see these free, noisy girls. He wanted to follow them, to talk to them while they watered their flocks.

He was confident he could make himself understood. Well-brought-up Egyptian boys, with a future as officials, were always taught basic Aramaic, so they could talk to the slaves. All the languages in this area were related. So he was sure he knew enough to talk a Midian girl round.

He walked behind them in the dust their sheep made.

At the well, amongst date trees, they hauled up water and poured it into stone troughs for their flock. They didn't seem to notice him. While they worked they sang a love song.

> *My love of all good love stands in the mountains yonder.*
> *My bear, my lion, my dove. Beyond the burning valley.*
> *I have no ass nor shoes for feet, to cross the valley to my sweet . . .*

They were all plump girls, well fed on mutton. He began to play a mental game which could loosely be called, *which one is prettiest?* One of them – fifteen or sixteen years old, and a sweet, ripe face. Some of the others older than that. Why aren't they married? he wondered.

He noticed with resentment some shepherds entering the oasis from the south. When they saw the girls, they came forward hooting, making faces like gorillas. They snatched up dust and threw it at the girls.

'How's your crazy old man?' they called.

It was as if the girls were used to having to quit the well. With crooks, they dragged their sheep away from the troughs and tried to stampede them, by stamping and hand-clapping, northwards through the trees, away from the invaders.

Moses jumped out in the girls' tracks. 'Go back,' he yelled. 'Go on. I'll fix it.' The girls stopped, probably because he still looked Egyptian. He marched into the well-clearing. One of the shepherds mimicked his walk for a second.

'What's the matter,' he asked the shepherds.

'They're a crazy family. Better if their flocks died, them along with their flocks.'

'They will first water their sheep.'

One of the shepherds said, 'Shepherds have been known to do terrible things to solo travellers. Even important ones.'

'I am travelling with the *bedu*. You will find them camped a little up the road. *Bedu* do dreadful things to shepherds.'

So the shepherds sat and waited and the girls came back. Prince Moses hauled the pail for them and filled the troughs. It was harder than he would have imagined. These girls must have arms as firm as rope. The thought of their arms distracted him, diminished his strength. So he suppressed the idea.

'Thank you, sir,' each of the girls told him as he filled the troughs.

'Where do you live?' he asked the one he liked best.

She didn't seem to want to answer, as if she was socially embarrassed. 'We are camped amongst tamarisks over there.'

'Can I visit you?'

'No one visits us.'

'I can't believe that.'

When the watering was over he walked away with the girls. He kept badgering the one he liked.

'What's your name then?'

'Zipporah.'

'Zipporah,' he said languorously. When you're infatuated, the girl's name takes on the same contours as the girl. 'You are going to take me home?'

'No. No one comes to our place.'

'Please.'

'No one.'

'Will you be back tomorrow?'

'We come every day.'

He went back to his tent highly disturbed. He was even a little hostile. Damn little desert mouse. No right to be stand-offish.

Next morning, through the early heat haze, he saw a woman crossing the valley. He thought,

> *I have no ass nor shoes for feet,*
> *To take me over to my sweet.*

It was Zipporah. All the tossing energies he had used up during the night had now materialised her.

'Sir,' she said, 'my father says that I was wrong. No one has ever lifted water for our sheep before. They think we are unclean.'

What does that mean? Moses asked himself. It means there is leprosy in the family.

'I do not mean unclean from disease,' the girl assured him. 'My father, though, was priest of his tribe and was expelled. Our people throw dust at us, as you know. It makes us impolite. I was impolite to you. I am sorry. My father asks if you would go to his tent and drink with him sheep's milk and eat mutton, cheese, and bread.'

'It is very kind of you.'

'I will wait upon you at table.'

'I'll get my horse now. You can ride with me.'

'Not yet,' she said. She pointed out features of the land that enabled him to find their tent. 'Give me time,' she said, 'to go home and prepare.'

In the afternoon he saddled his horse and rode in the direction she had told him. At last he saw on a knoll three tents. The families of Zipporah's brothers lived in the flanking two. There were spears and shields on display in front of the doors of the tents. These were meant to show that the family was not defenceless. I must be careful, Moses thought. The father will be very anxious to acquire another son, another bearer of arms.

In the desert there is only youth and then old age. Once the sun gets properly to a man's face, it is hard to tell whether he is thirty or fifty. So it was hard to tell the age of the man who now appeared in the flap of the main tent.

'You are an Egyptian?' he asked.

'I lack a nationality.'

'So do I. Come in. The meal is laid.'

Inside on a mat were all the desert delicacies. Dates and strong cheeses, confections of honey and honied locusts. Sour white wine to go with them. Before the mat sat Zipporah's two brothers. Zipporah herself and a mousey young woman who turned out to be her step-mother stood in a corner ready to serve, their heads bowed a little.

'I am Jethro,' the father said. 'I used to be a priest of the Midianite tribes. That is no longer.'

'No longer,' both the sons said.

And during the meal the story emerged. 'There is a mountain in the south called Horeb. Do you know it, young man? It is a terrible place. There is fire on its summit. We went down there one summer, following the coastal grasses.'

'Every second winter, round about, we go down there,' one of the brothers told Prince Moses.

'For the tribe that came with us,' Jethro continued, 'I sacrificed to the calf-god, to the goddess of the moon, to the sun-bird, to the snake, to the ibex, to all the tribes' gods. For every sacrifice I made I was of course paid, in one way or another. When we were camped in the Horeb area, I decided one afternoon to go up the mountain. I don't know why. I must confess, I'd been drinking a little. And Horeb was supposed to be a lucky mountain. It's a long climb and I was pretty breathless. When I got to the last slope below the summit, a wall of fire raced down the mountain towards me, a great wave of flame. I could feel the skin on my cheeks blistering.'

'He had blisters for weeks afterwards,' one of the sons said. No wonder, thought Moses. Sunburn.

'So I fell down. I kept my eyes clamped shut, I felt that if I opened them I'd be blinded. While I lay there I heard a babble of voices like a council meeting. And out of the voices, one voice came. No need to tell you it was a compelling voice. It said, "Jethro, you're the one who's been chosen to hear it. That there is no calf-god, moon-goddess, snake-god. I am god. Tell it to your tribe."'

'Tell your tribe,' one of the sons muttered. 'A hard thing to ask.'

Zipporah brought a pot of mutton stew and put it in front of the men. They began to dip into it with bread. Eating, Jethro went on:

'I said to the voice, I can't tell them that. Why would they believe me? They'd just think I was insane. Undermining my income like that. The voice said, you'll do it and survive because I am with you. Now it was a ravishing voice. I was spellbound all right. Then what is your name and your image? I asked. "My name is He," said the voice. "My name is the Voice. Stone idols are foul things to me." But, I said, they're just ordinary people. They won't understand you if you don't have an image. He said, if they want an image of my cleanliness, they may look at the moon. But they may not worship the moon, which I made with my hands.'

Prince Moses was frowning, and oddly disturbed. Why do I keep on running up against talk of one god who has no image? he asked himself. Or have desert dwellers always toyed with the idea of oneness?

'I told the voice, I had to have a sign,' Jethro said. 'The voice sighed and said all right. Look over at that thornbush over there, it said. I looked. I saw my head, very clearly, resting in the bush. Just my head, as if it had been sliced off my shoulders. Then the head started burning. Fire came out of its mouth. You can imagine how I felt. I yelled, enough, enough.'

The attention of the prince was caught half way between the story of Horeb and the face of Zipporah. Can I take her with me? he wondered. And if so, where will I go?

He asked Jethro, 'What happened when you came down the mountain?'

'Well, one gets over it when one comes down the mountain. Within a week, you have people pestering you to make sacrifices because a child or a ewe is sick. You can always find reasons to decide, well, I'll tell them the big news tomorrow. So I started sacrificing for my tribesmen again. And then one night . . . the boys saw it, didn't you? . . . one night a great box of fire seemed to come down through the roof of the tent. It dropped on my bed. My wife got up and ran out but I was more or less locked up in it. My wife and the boys came back and saw me wriggling there in that block of fire. They couldn't get near me.'

'We couldn't,' one of the boys said. '*Our* skin began to blister.'

'In the fire, He talked to me and asked me when? When was I going to speak up? And I made my final promises to Him and the fire lifted from me.'

'What did your tribesmen say when you told them?' Moses wanted to know.

'Stoned us, of course. We had to leave. We have no tribe.'

'No. It is a punishment, of course, for not having spoken sooner. I don't mind. In some ways it would have been easier had I not gone up the mountain. Yet I have Him.'

'*Have him?*'

'It is better,' said Jethro, 'to live in the truth even if one doesn't have a tribe.'

'Hear, hear.' said the brothers.

'In these tents He is loved.' Jethro said. 'The only thing is He could have chosen someone stronger.'

The weird idea buffeted the Egyptian's mind. A god who is loved? In these tents? By lovely Zipporah?

Jethro excused himself and went out to urinate.

While he was gone the brothers spoke softly to Moses.

'Do you desire our sister?' It sounded like an offer.

Moses was wary. 'I think she is very lovely.'

'And you would like to have her?'

'Yes. Isn't that natural enough?'

'Natural enough,' admitted one of the brothers.

'However,' said the other, 'a little group such as ours cannot afford to spend its women on good times for visitors. Also, He doesn't like it.'

'You can marry her, of course, in front of our father. He *is* a priest. But then you travel with us. And accept *Him* as your one god.'

Moses asked, 'Do you two rush all your visitors like this?'

'We don't have many visitors.'

The Lawgiver and the Voice

Back at the Bedouin camp, Moses spent three days arguing himself out of Zipporah. As an elegantly raised Egyptian, he did not savour the intimate tent life, the savage loyalties of Jethro's camp. More vaguely but more deeply, he was scared by the idea of Horeb and of the He who spoke on Horeb. You couldn't trust such a being. It might turn up at any time, making any demands. Improbably, it was *loved* in Jethro's tents.

On the third day he got to the well while the girls were watering the flocks. He took Zipporah to one side.

'Will you come with me? Away from your father? Away from that He?'

'Where would we go?'

'I don't know. Perhaps with the *bedu*. Then we would find our own place.'

She kept silent for half a minute. 'I will come with you. Why? If you went, all roads would be like water to me. I would not know where to put my feet.'

They began fondling each other. Moses quoted some lines from an Egyptian love poem.

> *If the chief physicians come to me,*
> *My heart is not satisfied with their medicines . . .*
> *When I see her, then will I be well.*
> *When she opens her eye, my body sings after its long silence.*

'Wait up tonight,' she told him. 'We must make a good distance before sunrise.'

But he could not account for what happened that night. Because when she came, towards midnight, he touched her face and her breasts once and said, 'It's no use. Let's go and wake your father.'

'Wake him?'

'There is nowhere for me to take you, my dove.'

And in that way an Egyptian prince became a desert herder with an exotic wife, strange relatives, and a positively perilous god who might make demands of a man on mountain tops.

He always liked to camp by the road from Elath and, meeting caravans, to ask them if Pharaoh Rameses was still alive.

In Egypt itself, the Crown Prince Merneptah thought of him and had the police question visiting businessmen about him. The people in Pithom, how-ever, lacked all news of him. Occasionally Aaron would say, 'He's dead, damn him.' As if dying in the desert were a very self-indulgent thing to do. Amongst children, old men, story-tellers, the account of Moses – secretly Israeli, visibly Egyptian prince, destroyer of an Egyptian overseer (or was it five, or twenty?) – was much favoured. Miriam let people know she be-lieved he was alive and sure to come back to Pithom. In spite of Aaron, this was the family view of Moses. Soon all of Pithom camp believed it.

Meanwhile Moses followed the seasons of a nomad with Jethro and the others. They grazed sheep where they were permitted to, in the valleys of Midian in the summer, then down the coast each side of the Gulf of Aqabah in winter. The pastures were harsh and juiceless compared to the places where Moses had grown up. The sheep were scraggy. Yet he loved all the people in his wife's small tribe. Because they were proud. Because they be-lieved they had inside knowledge.

One spring near Elath he heard from an Egyptian trader that the old Pharaoh Rameses was dead after seventy years of power. Cousin Merneptah

was now emperor of the red land and the black land. Moses wondered if he would ever hear from Merneptah. He didn't know whether he wanted to or not, but he thought about it a lot.

Beautiful Zipporah had by now carried and given birth to two sons. The first he called Gersam – the name meant *a stranger in a strange land*. The second was called Eliezer. His name meant, *help from Him*.

One year when they were all camped in the valley in Midian where Moses had first met Zipporah, they were visited by a trade expedition of Egyptians. These men camped down the slope below Jethro's place. Moses suspected their presence and stood outside his tent, squinting at their camp-fires, half the night.

Early in the morning, a dozen of them rode their horses right up to Jethro's door. They were armed. Zipporah's brothers came out through the flaps of their tents carrying spears. 'Stay there, brothers,' they called over their shoulders, as if were many more men indoors. In Moses' tent, Zipporah tried to pinion her husband. 'Don't go out,' she said.

One of the Egyptians had a snake-like blue-gold wand in his hand. He showed it, confident that they would understand. For it meant he was a royal officer.

'I have documents here signed by the emporor of all Egypt himself. My task is to put them in the hand of a certain Meses, or Moses, or Moishe or, as the Bedouin call him, Musa. This man is a cousin to almighty Merneptah. It would be ungracious of him not to accept these papers from me.'

One of Zipporah's brothers asked, 'You can't expect to find a man like that in this sort of place.'

'Come now. He married your sister. *That* we know from the Bedouin.'

Moses came out of his door. He spoke Egyptian. 'If you gave me the papers, I can assure you the man would get them.' In spite of his impediment, he spoke in a very courtly manner. The royal officer stared at him.

'Yes, I believe you would see to it that he read them, sir.'

He stretched out his hand, the papers in it, towards Moses. 'They certify your right to return freely, to resume your former status and office.'

'This cousin of Merneptah might like the office he has now.'

'Then you must remind him that as cousin of Merneptah, he has not only a place in the world but a duty. I say so with respect.'

'You have no authority to force this man to go back with you?'

'No authority.'

'One spring near Elath he heard from an
Egyptian herder that the old Pharaoh
Rameses was dead'

The Lawgiver and the Voice

'I am sure that this man Meses, Moses, Moishe, Musa, would want to send some of his love to His Highness Merneptah. He has fond memories of hunting crocodiles with the boy.'

'I suggest you urge the man to go to Merneptah and tell him these things himself.'

'He would have to think about that,' said Moses.

Moses put the papers away unopened and, that afternoon, the Egyptians moved on southwards.

Zipporah asked, 'Why do you hide them? It's a great thing to have an emperor write to you. Papers signed by his hand should be hung from the tent pole.'

'They would make me wonder.'

'Wonder?'

'In two prison camps, Pi-Rameses and Pithom, lie the members of what might well be my people. If I saw the letters all the time I would think every day: A man who gets letters from the Pharaoh ought to go to the Pharaoh and

say, you must let these Israeli Hapiru go their way. I don't want to make such a journey.'

In the winter Jethro's little tribe moved south, looking for the poor grass-lands which were all the other people of the earth had left for them. After many months, they camped under the mountain of Horeb. Jethro sacrificed one of his better lambs. When it had been gutted and properly portioned, he put its best parts on a fire. For this was the mountain of the Voice.

Then a preposterous thing happened. Admittedly desert tribesmen are very excitable. But even Moses saw this, or thought he did. As Jethro and his sons stood singing about the lovely grandeur of their god, smoke rose from the fire where the quarters of lamb were being burned. In reply, from the top of Horeb a thin ribbon of white smoke rose.

Seeing it, the family threw themselves down on the rubble of the slopes. Moses found himself in the same position. They sang and moaned; it was all ecstasy. The vast being who had separated them from their tribe and most of their income had now answered them. They were a valid people now. He was courting them the way a young man courts a girl.

Moses wasn't as happy. In fact he was frightened. He thought, up there is el Shaddai who shut off the hearing of the Egyptian overseer. What else will he do to me?

Now I must say that around the springs in this area there grows a grass which, if burnt and inhaled, makes a person see fantastic creatures and events that deny all sense. I am not saying that this explains all or even any of the strange events round Horeb or later on. In fact I never saw Moses, in the years I knew him, inhale the stuff. I suppose I mention it only so that people will not think I am naïve.

When the excitement was over, Moses spoke to Jethro. 'Are you going up to the mountain?'

'Not unless I am told to. It's disturbing up there. You feel you're going to fly apart. After all, I'm only a timid man. But you, maybe you should go up.'

'Me? Why do you say that?' For a second Moses thought his father-in-law was some sort of conspirator.

'You want to go up. I can tell it. And the Voice, the *He*, maybe He wants you to go up too.'

'I have enough to do down here.'

'I would wait till mid-afternoon if I were you. Take plenty of rugs if you intend to stay the night.'

'I don't intend anything.'

Yet he *knew* he was going to climb the mountain. He went to his tent.

'Zipporah my love, I want a wallet with dried fruit. I want a water flask. I want my staff.'

Almost ceremonially, she got the flask and the wallet and hung them from his neck. Then she handed him his sheperd's staff.

Frowning she said, 'If it says, go to Egypt, tell it your woman Zipporah and your two sons beg it to let you off. Beg it to find someone else.'

'Yes, dove,' he said. He meant it. Then and there he began the climb. His sisters-in-law wailed to see him go.

I have been to that mountain. It is a red-brown sterile mountain. If you took the finger of a child and measured it – that's how much rain falls there each year. It is just enough to keep a few tangled acacia bushes in existence. As you climb a mountain like that, the sun sits on your shoulder. It weighs a hot ton. The hot air goes down your throat like cinders.

Close to the top, he saw the now famous thorn bush. It was burning but, inside the flame, he could see each small branch. He thought, this has to be looked at. A bush that's on fire yet doesn't burn. He felt no fear now that the strange things had begun. As he got closer, he heard a great babble of voices coming out of the bush and one moaning voice like his own, a voice that had an impediment, that was trying to speak. He sweated for it to begin talking, as one does sweat for a stammerer. Then it found words. First it said them in Miriam's voice, then in Amram's, then a voice that went through you like a knife.

This is what it said: 'Come no closer. Take your shoes off your feet. You are standing on sacred ground.'

Moses obeyed.

The Voice said, 'I am the god your fathers have always honoured, the el Shaddai of Abraham and Isaac and Jacob.'

Moses knew that these were names out of the tribal history of the Israeli Hapiru. He had heard them as a fugitive in Pithom. Now he got an urge to hide his face from the blazing bush, the voice that named so clearly his fathers.

'I have not been blind,' the Voice told him. 'to the tyranny my people suffer in Egypt. I have heard their complaints about the cruelty of their taskmasters. I know all their sorrows. I have come down to rescue them from the power of the Egyptians. To lead them away into a good land, a large country, into a land that is all milk and honey. Yes, the cry of Israel's race has come to my ears. Therefore get up, I want you to take a message to Pharaoh's court. You are to lead my people, the sons of Israel, out of Egypt.'

Moses, on the ground, hands over his eyes, began stammering. 'Who I am that I ought to go to Pharaoh? Why should I be the one to bring the Israelis out of Egypt?'

His own awkward voice answered him out of the bush. El Shaddai was using the stammer for teaching purposes. 'I . . . will be . . . with you. And when you have brought . . . my people out of Egypt . . . you will find your-self back here . . . sacrificing to me on this mountain.'

Moses asked the deadly question. 'If I tell the Israelis, the god of your fathers has sent me to you, and if they say, what is his name? What do I say to them then?'

'You shall say to them he is called what he is. I am the god *Who Is*. You shall tell the Israelis, the god *Who Is* has sent me to you. My name is Yahweh. My name is *I-am-that-I-am*. You will tell them that Yahweh is the name I will be known by for ever. It shall stand recorded, age after age.'

'Yahweh,' said Moses. '*I-am-that-I-am*.'

'First meet with the leaders of the Israelis. Tell them their god has spoken to you. With them, make your way into the presence of the king of Egypt. Now I am sure the king of Egypt will not let you go, no, not unless there is strong compulsion. I must therefore exert my power and strike Egypt with all my wonders. I will also let you have your way with the Egyptians. You shall take a toll from them. Gold and silver ornaments, and clothes to dress your sons and daughters.'

'What if . . . what if they tell me to my face: That I haven't seen you?'

'What's that in your hand?'

Moses looked up. He saw he still had his shepherd's staff in his hand. 'A staff,' he said.

'Throw it on the ground.'

Moses stood up and threw the staff on the ground. As soon as it touched earth, it was transformed into one of those long, highly venomous snakes, their skins colourful as woven blankets, that one finds in the area. It began to crawl away.

'Quick,' said the Voice, 'take it by the tail.'

Now Moses had a phobia of snakes, all his life. He was nonetheless able somehow to stretch out and grab the tail. Immediately – and if you don't believe me, you can comfort yourself by remembering the exotic grass that grows by wells – it turned back into a staff.

The Voice said, 'If they see things like that, will they still doubt that you saw me?'

From the bush there was a sort of silence for half a minute, though you could still hear that strange babble of all the voices and languages you had ever known. At last the voice spoke again for itself.

'Put your hand inside your clothes.'

Moses obeyed.

'Now take it out again.'

He took it out slowly, wondering what he was going to see. When he got the hand out, it was dead white and ulcerated. It was in fact the hand of a leper. Moses tried frantically to shake it off. But the voice told him to return it to his clothing and take it out again. After he'd done that, the hand was its normal self again.

'If they will not believe you for either of these signs, then take water from the river and pour it on the ground. The water you draw out of the river will turn to blood.'

He won't be talked round, Moses thought in a panic. 'Elohim, el Shaddai, god who is, I am not eloquent. Now that you have spoken to me, I am more tongue-tied than ever.'

This little speech did not appease the Voice. 'Who has made man's mouth? Who makes the dumb or deaf or the seeing or the blind? Is it not I? If you want a spokesman, your brother Aaron shall be the man. You shall put the staff in his hand. But with you shall be the power of the lord Yahweh.'

When he looked again at the bush, it still burned, there was a small twittering of voices in it. But then the fire died altogether, and the voices went.

Feverish, Moses staggered off downhill. He wanted to get down into the valley, to his tent and Zipporah.

The Lawgiver goes Home

When Zipporah heard, she said, 'What I knew in my blood has been proved right.'
There were debates with Jethro. 'Don't disobey him,' Jethro urged. 'Are you so frightened of him?'

'He is my all. One does not disobey one's all.'

Therefore, within a few weeks, the tribe began moving north. Jethro wanted to speed the pace up, but Moses delayed all he could. Perhaps one night, the voice of Yahweh would enter his tent and say, 'I can see you are not the right man. Never mind, we can still be friends.'

In telling the story, I have to keep saying. 'Then an amazing thing happened . . .' All I can say about what happened then is that it was pretty startling. I got confused accounts from Moses and from Zipporah, his lovely Midianite woman.

Zipporah was woken up one night by the noise of Moses arguing with himself in sleep. Her eyes not yet open, she reached out a hand to touch him. His flesh felt as hot as metal. She opened her eyes. Her husband looked like a man on fire. It was as if he were glass and the fire and heat were streaming through him. She knew that fire was a sign of the presence of the god of Horeb. The fire was eating him up because he was dawdling in Sinai. She could smell the displeasure of Yahweh under the tent roof.

'What? What?' she yelled. Yet as soon as she said it she knew what to do. Both her boys were sleeping in a corner. Frenzied, she reached for the elder one. She hauled him out of his sleep and across the floor by the ankle. Naturally, Gersam, who was two years old, squealed mightily. 'It won't be long, love,' she said, speaking equally to the boy and to Moses. She found Moses' knife. She was sure that only the blood sacrifice of her child would work. But then she thought, no, I won't give that. Blood sacrifices are made to stone idols, not to true gods. She grabbed the child's foreskin and tried to hack it off. Naturally, he was able to crawl away after the first stroke of the knife. She had to sit on him. As she had promised, she did it quickly.

The baby crawled away into a corner, screaming and clutching his maimed genitals. Zipporah held up the foreskin and then, in spite of heat, dripped its blood onto Moses' feet, picked up the child himself, and dripped his blood flow on its father.

She said 'Now we are betrothed in blood.'

The fire left Moses. He lay heaving for breath. 'Now I know why my people circumcise,' he said at last. By his people he meant the Hapiru Israelis.

The horse he had first ridden out of Egypt, across Sinai into Midian, was now aged and scrawny from eating sour grass. Nonetheless he mounted it the next morning, leaving Jethro and Zipporah and little Gersam, the boy still querulous with pain.

In Pithom Miriam and Aaron went through a family punching-and-biting session. Aaron had had a dream. He had been standing at the Lake Timsah ferry, feeling very uncomfortable. Beside him stood Pharaoh Merneptah. Aaron was surprised how nervous Merneptah was. Together, they were waiting for someone to come out of the desert. Out of the haze of salt and hot air above the lake, the ferry approached them. The ferryman had no face. Merneptah began to tremble. When the ferry touched sand, a terrible lion, who seemed to drip sparks of light onto the earth, jumped at Merneptah and disembowelled him as neatly as an embalmer would. Then the lion demanded

Aaron's hand on its mane and led him back onto the ferry, and so into the
desert. Aaron woke with a thirst.

Aaron could not stop himself from talking about this dream. He suspected
what it meant. That his brother Prince Moses was in the desert, travelling
towards Egypt. He knew too, but didn't say aloud, that he should go out and
meet him. And when Miriam said so, in her shrewish way, he thought the
only thing to do was to shut her up with a beating. It was not one-sided
however. Miriam had an arm as long as any man's. 'I have to live in the
present,' he said at last, as an apology. 'I can't live by dreams. That's a luxury for wealthy Egyptians.'

'So you live like a dog. Panting for the next handout of stale fish and corn-
bread. Bow wow!'

'I've never been near the desert. I believe it takes money to survive there.
I believe dreams have no face value there.'

'What if I got you the money?'

'How? Whoring? You flatter yourself.'

'Damn your eyes. I'll steal it.'

And she did. From a drunk in Pithom market. With half of it she bribed
the overseer to cover Aaron's absence. The other half she gave to Aaron.

He wasn't used to having money, or moving large distances at will. Once
across Timsah, in the great spaces, he would talk to himself. 'I know how
slavery's made me soft, brother. I wish I had my slavery back. Free from
making up one's mind. Free from doing anything except what one is threatened into doing. A terrible thing, freedom.'

In the camps at Pithom and Pi-Rameses the news of Aaron's unlikely
journey, and what it might mean, got round. Not all the slaves were happy
about it. One of the three Israelis who had seen the overseer killed, a Pithom
foreman called Dathan, felt that the return of Prince Moses would do no good
and only make things tougher for ordinary people. He went and made a
statement to a junior police official. The Pharaoh would want to know, he
said. His impetuous cousin was coming back.

For some reason this report was shelved or lost.

Somewhere out in the Wilderness of Paran, the brothers met. Cynics might
say: By one of those wells that grow narcotic grass?

Whatever happened there transformed Aaron, turned him from an amenable slave into a rabid spokesman, who himself could perform the wonders
of the leper's hand and the snake.

When they came together down the road from Succoth many of the
people in Pithom camp came out to meet and cheer them. Miriam herself.

'Brother, my husband is dead in a work's accident. I have only my children, Rachel and Liah. So I can devote myself to the cause.'

After his long journey the crowd and Miriam made him nervous. 'How do you know there's a cause?' he asked Miriam.

'There's always been one,' she said.

He presented himself and his papers to the commissioner in Pithom city. 'My brother goes with me,' he told the commissioner.

'Your brother?' asked the commissioner.

'Yes. Aaron.'

'Yes, sir.' The commissioner suspected the royal cousin of suffering from desert madness. But he made no objections.

First though, Moses wanted a meeting with the foremen, chairmen of barrack and street councils, and other leaders in Pithom camp. Aaron, spokesman, did the arguing. Moses was a sort of chairman and commentator. He found that his stammer was much worse since his experience on Horeb.

Many of the men at this meeting showed they had the mental disease of all slaves. Since they were slaves and their masters were not, their masters' way of life must be better than their old way of life. Their masters' gods must be stronger than the shepherds' god they brought out of the desert with them.

Dathan, a foreman, made an angry speech. 'There is only trouble for us in taking up with that hoary old god from the desert again. If that god is the one god then he is the one who made us slaves. Unless there's a god of freedom and a god of slavery. In that case we're back with many gods.'

'Slavery is to try us,' Aaron said. 'The way a man tries a girl before he knows she is loyal.'

'Then I say what many girls say. I don't want to be put to tests.'

After this, members of the meeting began asking for the signs Moses was supposed to have brought from the desert. Aaron looked at his brother.

'No. No. Don't give them any sign. Tell them by the time we've talked to Merneptah, they'll be glutted with signs.'

A lot of people were won over by this attitude. There are always some slaves whose rebelliousness runs close to the surface. But Dathan's party kept their view. It was this:

'There is a real land and its name is Egypt. Its power is more than a normal person can grasp. This is the fact of our lives. Whispers from the desert mean nothing.'

The Lawgiver and the bloody River

Aaron and Moses rode together north to Pi-Rameses. They left behind them in Pithom groups who would nag and plan towards the day of tribal escape.

By presenting his papers all the way, Moses at last walked into the palace with his spokesman. They found its lobbies crowded with plump noblemen in transparent shirts, expensive women with pads of perfume on their cheeks.

'There's to be a reception later today,' said the guards' officer who carried Moses' papers.

They were led into a living-room large as a village. In one far corner sat Pharaoh, thinner than his grandfather, frowning. His crown, shaped like a harp, bordered with gold snakes, lay on a table close by. Near-by, his Nubian wife, black and lovely, bending over a cradle. The child it contained was crying. Three shaven-skulled physicians stood by. They must have been treating the child for some illness.

Moses waited till the Pharaoh's eye fell on him, and bowed.

'Arabs?' said the Pharaoh, on account of their desert clothes.

'No, my lord. You remember me. I grew up in Bubastis and took you hunting.'

'My cousin. *My cousin*. I can tell the impediment . . . the stammer . . . why do you wear those clothes?'

'Because, Highness, I have been travelling.'

'Take the boy out, my love,' said Pharaoh to the queen.

A nurse carried the boy outside. The queen also went, looking at Moses a second out of eyes heavily blackened with kohl. The priests, mum-faced experts in Egypt's mighty sciences, stayed.

'My boy,' said Merneptah, 'doesn't keep food down. There is something wrong with his blood.'

'It will be amended,' said one of the physicians.

'Royal blood is the blood of Horus,' Pharaoh said. 'Stars flow in it. Yet there's something wrong with my son's. Have you children, cousin?'

'Yes.'

'In a distant place?'

'Yes, sir.'

'Is their blood tainted?'

'''"Royal blood is the blood of Horus,"
Pharaoh said. "Stars flow in it. Yet there's
something wrong with my son's"'

OVERLEAF '''I've developed other passions.
A man often does"'

'No, Highness.'

The Pharaoh closed his eyes, absorbing the puzzle. 'Come up to me,' he said. 'I want to hold you.'

Moses obeyed. Merneptah put hands round Moses' shoulders and inclined his head till it rested against his cousin's dusty chest. He was smaller than Rameses, both in body and in manner.

'I remember you as I remember the gazelles and crocodiles. I remember too your voice. How I even went through a phase when I imitated you. I drove my tutors mad. I was too young to say then, I want him by my side.'

'And you're old enough now?'

The Pharaoh sat up. 'Yes. And king of the world. And when I open my mouth, gods talk. Are you still a lady killer?'

'I've developed other passions. A man often does.'

'Does he? Didn't you ever hear my voice calling you across the wasteland?'

'No. Other voices.'

'Yes. Desert voices. We all know about them. Less coherent than drunks. Here, by the river, we have words under our control. They are our animals. Firm sharp animals; firmly, sharply arranged. We make a firm, sharp world with them. A wide world. All ours. From now on, you will help manage it.'

'It's no use, sir,' Moses said. 'In the desert . . .'

'Yes, yes? You have some woman there?'

'Yes. But even more. I heard firmer, sharper words there.'

Merneptah closed his eyes again. Moses could sense the hurt in him. He isn't a bad man, interested in justice, a little spoiled, but pleasant. Why am I under orders to do him harm?

Meanwhile, Merneptah pointed at his priest-physicians.

'These men are the elite when it comes to words. Were *they* there?'

'No.'

'Then you heard nothing. You have come back to me. And to the firm word. Have a little gratitude to grandfather Rameses. Not to mention dear Aunt Hathi . . .'

'I have to tell you. There is no avoiding it. *This* is my brother. Yes, my brother. Accept it please, Highness, for the moment. Now if I say what must be said it will take a long and painful time. Let him say it. Please.'

'By all means,' said Merneptah, half amused.

And so, from fascination, Pharaoh let a glib Hapiru slave speak up in his living-room. Aaron gave an account of Horeb and then asked what his brother had already decided should be asked. Since it was not permitted to sacrifice to desert gods inside Egypt, Merneptah must let the Israelis go into the desert to sacrifice to the god *Who Is*.

'"If my brother is sent away, I will starve myself. There are wonders he hasn't shown you yet"'

OVERLEAF 'Merneptah's physicians and Aaron in the palace at Pi-Rameses'

When Aaron was finished, Pharaoh sat making faces. At last he said, 'It's painful. To see a cousin go this way.'

All at once he was very angry and stood up, ranting. 'I don't know this confounded god. Listen, we deal in *world* politics here. It is beneath our dignity to give *one* tribe of Hapiru leave so that they can kill sheep out in Sinai. There is such a thing as order too – you know we have no favourites among the slave races, we treat them all well by the standards of other king-doms. If I let your Israelis go, I'd have to let all the Hapiru go. Otherwise even slaves can see, plain as day, that Pharaoh lacks divine justice. And if the Hapiru, the hundreds of thousands of them, all with a desert god of their own, why not let the Nubians go too? The proposition is an insult.'

'Not intended,' said Moses.

'You have a desert lunacy, damn it! You dare to have a desert lunacy. But there is a cure.'

'It can be amended,' said one of the physicians.

'Anyhow, I think this. I think any god who sulks on a hill in the wasteland and says he's better than all the Nile gods, I think he's a provincial, a hick god. If . . . *if* . . . he is any sort of god, why doesn't he come to town, so to speak, present himself to the government of Egypt?'

'It is intended,' said Moses.

'Do you know this was supposed to be a happy time?'

'I am sorry.'

'You shall not go. You shall stay here, under house arrest till you're better. Your *brother* will be . . .'

'If my brother is sent away, I will starve myself. There are wonders he hasn't shown you yet.'

'Are there, are there? I wonder what they can be. The trick with the rod perhaps, that turns into a snake? You should remember. I have the greatest cursers, magicians, physicians and diviners in existence. That's all.'

'For your kingdom's sake,' said Moses, 'we should not be separated.'

For some reason, Merneptah consented. He was probably curious. There is no Egyptian who is not fascinated by signs, white and black. 'For a time,' said Merneptah. 'Only for a time.'

As Moses and his spokesman were led out, Pharaoh called out to his cousin. 'You know you've spoiled my day? You are under command to get better.'

Locked in one of the poorer apartments at Pi-Rameses, Moses talked about the audience with his brother.

'We should have threatened him.'

'*Threatened?*'

'Of course. It is what is ordered.'

Moses began to tremble. He had to be led to a bed.

'What will I threaten him with?' Aaron asked.

'Plagues, catastrophes, political disasters. Death in his family.' He put his forearm over his eyes.

'I felt certain when I met you out in Sinai. It's harder to feel certain in there.'

'I don't find it hard,' his brother said. 'I wish I did.'

When the Israeli Hapiru heard that Prince Moses had made demands for them in front of Merneptah, they got very stimulated. They seemed to believe Merneptah had somehow taken up a challenge. This gave them a new sense of importance. They were less amenable at their work. Their attitude was reported to Merneptah as significant.

One of the old Pharaoh's ministers, whom Merneptah had inherited, gave him some advice.

'Your grandfather had a method of keeping people in the slave camps too busy to think of their old life. Without reducing the tally of bricks to be made or laid, he withheld supplies of straw, so that to make the bricks they had to gather or cut their own straw. Of course the overseers had to be very sharp and not allow any exceptions.'

The executive order was given.

Israeli foremen knew they were middle men and likely to suffer a lot of thugging from above if daily brick tallies were not up to normal. They visited Pi-Rameses' palace with a petition to Merneptah. In a yard they passed Moses and Aaron, who were strolling with Nubian guards.

'It's good to see our leaders living well,' one of the foremen called.

'You take your damned ease. While we're given higher production targets.'

The foremen were not let into the Pharaoh's presence but permitted to hand their petition to some palace official. Walking out disappointed they had even more to say.

'Yahweh ought to be told this,' they yelled. 'You've made our name stink in Pharaoh's nostrils. His court doesn't want a sniff of us. You put a rod in their fists for us. Tomorrow it will be a sword. *You! You!*'

They stood hissing at Moses and wouldn't move till the Nubians threatened them. They were still screaming as they vanished out of a gateway.

Moses stood sweating. The Israelis were first-born of the god Who Is, el Shaddai, Elohim, Yahweh. Their flesh was not made for lashing. He began calling out then, in the garden.

'I talked to Merneptah,' he called, his voice breaking, the words broken and lumpy. 'I spoke in your name. In front of the king of names I used *your name*. And since then he does nothing except misuse my race. Is this the freedom you send them?'

'Calm down,' Aaron said, frightened. He didn't believe in taking on the god *Who Is* face to face.

The Nubians, who had orders to put the royal cousin inside again if he became excited, hustled him back to his apartment.

As the new order began to bite into the Israeli Hapirus in the slave camps at Pi-Rameses and Pithom, the slaves lost interest in Prince Moses. So much so that a physician suggested Moses ought to be let go, to taste close up the bitterness of the Israelis.

'Mightn't he get dangerous?' a minister asked Merneptah. 'Isn't there a record of homicide . . . ?'

'That was an accident,' said Merneptah.

Aaron and Moses were let go and again faced meetings in both camps. Aaron had to speak in the face of loud catcalls and thrown stones. There were pockets of approval. But approval hasn't as deep a voice as hate.

Still, whenever Moses was alone or asleep, the Voice harried him. The Voice always went with some form of fire, and sometimes he felt the fire was in his belly.

And there were more audiences with Merneptah. Audiences were easily arranged because Merneptah was fascinated. First, by the nature of Moses' disease. Second, by the threat of wonders performed by Aaron. Again the Egyptian love of wonders and scientific demonstrations. In fact that's what caused Merneptah his trouble: His interest in Moses was a luxury, a self-indulgence. Grandpa Rameses would not have allowed himself such luxuries. He would have had Moses locked up in the country and then murdered as a family embarrassment.

There are a lot of stories about evening confrontations between Merneptah's physicians and Aaron in the palace at Pi-Rameses. The physicians mostly bald, poker-faced, unblinking. Aaron moving with small steps and half-embarrassed gestures. Like a slave in fact, yet confident. He had begun to get that terrible confidence his brother had spoken of. Even when stones were landing on their platform. Even when faced with the college of physicians.

The air, on the nights these confrontations took place, must have sizzled with the powers of the parties involved.

In the most popular story, Aaron – on an invitation from Merneptah – threw his staff on the tiled floor. It became a serpent. Merneptah laughed and called on his men, who threw their staffs down. These two became fat vipers. In a way snakes never do in real life, the snakes of the physicians surrounded Aaron's snake as if they would embed their teeth in it on all sides. But Aaron's snake ate all theirs, and then Aaron picked his up and it became a staff again. The physicians were pretty distressed at losing their staffs, which were signs of their status. Merneptah, however, was the one who got most dangerously angry. He ordered his college of physicians to leave the room. 'I suspend your qualifications,' he roared. They left. No doubt they were back within a week, at work with new staffs cut to the proper length and striped appropriately.

Now I mention – just for fairness – that this sort of snake story is a favourite one with many peoples. It's told of many legendary magicians. I don't for a moment condemn any storyteller for using it in connection with Moses and Aaron. I simply remark that it turns up in a lot of romances. Like the story of Moses being both a slave child and a prince. Well, of both the stories, I personally think the one about the basket on the beach at Bubastis is probably true. But the one about the big snake?

After one such evening, Merneptah ordered Moses and Aaron to be arrested again and locked in palace bedrooms.

Now not even a person like me can deny that voices strike people out of the dark, that strange demands can come out of the air. That having heard the Voice, people change as Moses changed. So this happened, or something like it. Merneptah would sometimes receive petitions by the river bank at Pi-Rameses. And the Voice told Moses to interrupt him there and make the demands again. And if they were refused, Aaron was to hit the shallows with his staff and the river would become diseased.

It was a mouthful to ask any person raised in Egypt to harm the river. The river was Egypt's greatest being, and bride to the sun. But whatever the mental problems the idea carried for Moses, he still had this weird confidence: He could order Aaron to do it. And the result would be disease.

The two house-guests, cousin Moses and his common spokesman, broke into Merneptah's early morning stroll. Merneptah ordered them removed, but before it could be done Aaron had whipped the shallows with his staff. The two of them were very roughly bundled back indoors, Moses stammering, 'It will turn to blood.'

Merneptah was panting with anger. 'How dare he have such intentions! Against the river!'

'Something should be done about him,' one of the ministers said.

'Yes,' Merneptah said, but was strangely unwilling. His cousin's illness had him engrossed.

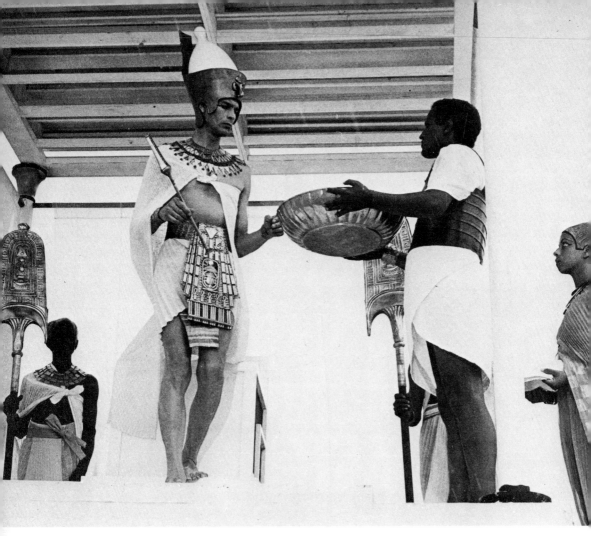

Back in his apartments, Moses brooded. 'A frightful thing,' he said. 'A blood river.'

That the river might turn to blood was one of the common terrors of Pharaohs. It's happened once or twice, according to the records. In fact, the water doesn't turn to blood that's like an animal's blood. It's worse than that. A great rusty red tide comes downstream, thick, smelly. It invades all the backwaters, where it spreads like something living. It floats like a scum on the waters of the main channels. The fish die, the river's stench is worse than unattended-to corpses. The water cannot be drunk. If this *blood* is even a little bit in the water, it kills anyone who drinks.

Some say the blood occurs because of events far upstream in the unvisited countries where the river begins. Up there, according to legends, it rains half the year, amazing quantities of rain. And in the rain and fog, fabulous animals die, mud-bound. And great trees go under, and rot. The rusty scum is the foul off-product of all this.

The question is: How did Moses know the blood was coming downstream? Pharaoh had distant warning-posts but *he* didn't know.

Within a little time – two or three days – the tide came downstream. Merneptah's college of physicians took samples of it, tested its density, sang to it, threatened it with their staffs and promised they could remove it within a week.

All that week Moses and Aaron were locked up and not once called on. To ask Aaron to join his powers to those of the college was more than Merneptah could manage.

The brothers knew that outside their sealed quarters there must be pressure on the king to have them executed. They could smell the frightening reek of the river – it got in even through locked doors.

The Israelis in Pi-Rameses were delighted by the bloody river. It meant the great symbols of Egyptian power could go rotten overnight. To stop them from reaching these conclusions, and so that they could be better supervised, the government now moved those who lived in Pi-Rameses camp and crowded them into Pithom with the other half of the tribe. Control was harsh there now: the camp was thoroughly guarded.

This was Merneptah's mistake. Once more, his grandfather wouldn't have made it. Because it gave the tribe a unity. Even those foremen, like Dathan, who thought co-operation with Egypt was the only sane way, now saw Merneptah was too angry to accept their respect, their goodwill.

Somehow, Joshua, Caleb and other rebels kept Moses informed of all this by smuggled messages. Amongst the common Israeli slaves, they said, the name of the god who turned Egypt's river to blood was repeated again and again.

Another side to Merneptah's mistake was this: By moving all the Israelis to Pithom, he kept them clear of the river, and of the river bank areas where most of the other troubles struck. So other people and the Israelis themselves began to believe that the tribe had been exempted from disaster.

After a week the blood river began to clear, as the college of physicians had predicted it would. So, as far as Merneptah was concerned, the science of Aaron had been answered by the science of the physicians.

He had Moses and Aaron brought into his state-room so that he could explain it to them.

'It will always be so,' he said. 'My servants will always have an answer for you.'

'For . . . for frogs?' asked Moses.

'For frogs,' said Aaron, 'that swarm in the river, make their way into your house?'

'Frogs,' Merneptah said, and shuddered.

'Frogs can in any case be expected, Highness,' a senior physician said. 'Once the bloody water is sent us, frogs follow.'

'Why wasn't my cousin a good cousin? He sends us the foul water. But even my college says yes, frogs will follow the foul water.'

'King, if you don't like frogs,' Aaron informed him, 'there is a way to avoid them.'

'Listen. If I let you go, I am saying this. That the wonders of a desert god overpower the wonders of Egypt's company of divinities. My power, the power I have over you this second, comes from these divinities. If I let you go I say my power is second class. It is not second class. Now, I could have you skinned and eviscerated at night by willing hands. But I want a better punishment than that. I want to see you here, admitting with tears that the settled and magnificent science of Egypt is the supreme science. That there is nothing to learn from voices in the desert.'

But, as Merneptah had never seen the bloody water, he'd never seen such frogs. Matting the withering lawns of Pi-Rameses, fouling the tiles of the open galleries. According to what's accepted by the Israelis now, he called on Moses and Aaron to pray the plague of frogs away. I wonder. A strange thing for a king to do who wants to save face.

However, in one day, all the frogs that had come out of the river, infesting the streets and households of every city on the river, died on dry land. The stench was worse than the bloody river had been. And in the smell of rotting frog corpses, of course, was the promise of more evils.

At the next audience Aaron said there would be gnats and flies. And there were gnats and flies everywhere, clouds of the insects. Animals went mad, rushed into the river. The bites festered on humans. Even in the best houses, people sat at home with their heads under blankets or sheeting. Peasants caught in the open by a swarm were bitten to the point of madness. They drowned themselves in irrigation ditches rather than take another sting.

I have seen flies like that. Little man-eaters that take flesh out of you each time they bite.

According to the Israeli legends that are most quoted now, in my old age, Merneptah again called on Moses and Aaron to chant the flies away. According to the legends too, Merneptah was so anxious to be rid of the cannibal flies that he offered to let the Israelis go three days into the desert if Moses and Aaron made the flies vanish. And then, when the flies vanished, he wouldn't keep his promise.

I wonder if even privately he could have made that sort of offer in the first place. His state of mind would have been, if Egyptian scientists can't find a cure, then there is no cure.

Probably what happened was that Aaron and Moses would send a verbal offer to the state-room. We'll get rid of the flies for you if you let the tribe leave Pithom and go into the desert – that sort of offer. They might have got a sarcastic reply. It was to be a while yet before Merneptah would take them seriously.

Whether it was from the flies or the rotting frog flesh or traces of the rust-red poison in the water animals drank, farm animals all along the river began to die. There is nothing that unsettles a king as much as receiving reports from up and down the river that wealthy pastoralists have been wiped out, prominent cattle farmers have lost all their stock. Merneptah was getting so obsessed with cousin Moses and the claims he made for the Hapiru Israelis, that he sent some official to Pithom, to find out if sheep and cattle were dying in the area around the camp. Of course, he found they weren't.

You might say that this further immunity was due not only to the god *Who Is*, but also to the distance of Pithom from the river, the rotting frogs, the fly swarms. Surprisingly, Egyptians wouldn't think that way. Their river is a vein in the great throat of a god. It is the best and safest place to live in the world. Therefore, Merneptah would think, if these things are happening by the river, they ought to be even worse over there, near Pithom, in the grasslands. The news that they weren't worse made him more unbalanced still.

Next time there was an audience, Moses and Aaron took pouches filled with cinders from the oven in their apartment. They made the normal useless demands and then took handfuls of the cinders and threw them towards the ceiling.

Merneptah had them bustled out. 'Fouling my house,' he screamed after them. 'Fouling my house!'

'There'll be ulcers,' said Aaron from the door. 'There'll be boils.'

'Skin infections could be expected,' the dean of the college of physicians said, 'after such catastrophes.'

'All you do,' Merneptah complained, 'is tell me that what they predict is possible. Such a passive role is an insult to the idea of Egypt. We impress ourselves on events, not the other way round. Will I tell you what I am sick of? I am sick of having my cousin do things to me. And hearing you say afterwards, it's quite normal, it's to be expected.'

Because of Moses' trust in the god *Who Is*, neither he nor Aaron suffered in the epidemic of abscesses and swellings of the skin. Boils and blisters put

'"Skin infections could be expected,"
the dean of the college of physicians said,
"after such catastrophes"'

the entire college of physicians in bed. Merneptah saw the appearance of even the smallest ulcer on the flesh of his servants as an act of their political disobedience. Since even his sickly little boy got them on his body, Merneptah sat in his state-room feeling betrayed. The god *Who Is* knew how to sap the sanity of a weak king.

What happened next, like all the rest, was something that doesn't often happen in the delta. A great hailstorm came in from the north. Lumps of ice as big as your fist fell out of the sky. Besides braining many farm-workers and some of the cattle that had survived the earlier epidemics, it flattened out and destroyed the flax harvest and the barley crop. Merneptah woke

from an afternoon sleep to see the hail come down. There was violent lightning. He hated lightning. After two hours he sent for Moses.

'Cousin, will you make it stop?'

The minister and the secretary who were in the room at the same time both gave the Pharaoh advice. 'Don't give in to him now, Highness. Hail-storms aren't unknown. It will be over by evening.'

The Pharaoh averted his face from them and sat shuddering. 'Cousin, can you make it stop?'

In his early experiences of *He Who Is*, the first rosy season of his relationship with Yahweh, Moses never hesitated to make such promises. 'If you let the Israelis go,' he repeated. So he walked out of the palace, through the garden, down to the river to stop the hail and lightning. Within five minutes the sun was out again.

'These storms always stop suddenly,' said the minister.

'You will let them go?' asked Moses.

'I will not. There are doubts. Who stopped it? You? My servants? Horus..?'

Next and worst, a sirocco blew a great cloud of locusts up from Ethiopia. They settled on the crops the hail had left. The world was full of the noise of their whirring, of their jaws busy on every piece of greenery. Every fruit tree was stripped. Too late, a violent west wind came out of the land of the dead and blew the swarms out into the Red Sea.

Of all these disasters the college of physicians said, 'Taking the plagues one by one, each one was normal and we were able to control its severity by the force of our science and our incantations. That they should all come at once, in the same season, is unfortunate. It must mean something. That the divinities under whom we live are not pleased with Egypt's present fibre.'

The seasons turned and Egypt got its normality back. Pharaoh had Moses and Aaron brought to him a last time. 'You have done your worst, cousin Moses, and Egypt is still a nation. And we still sit here, while your damned tribe sits on the ground. Your desert being has given up. Does he still bother even to talk to you?'

'King, the god *Who Is* still speaks to me.'

'What if I gave you all leave to go into the desert? Wives, children. But not your animals. You leave your animals here as a tax.'

'No . . . a people needs its livestock with it. We don't know what we will be asked to sacrifice to the lord Yahweh. Also, we don't intend to die out there, without animals, without meat or milk!'

'I would have thought your magic god could have fed you.'

'He has not yet guaranteed *that*.'

Merneptah got very excited and stood up. 'That's why I think perhaps you are a slave. *He has not yet guaranteed it!* If I had such a mean and slavish attitude towards the gods of Egypt, they would break my bones, and with some justice. Well, I tell you this. No more comfortable house arrest for you. It's Pithom, amongst the slaves, for you. And take good care. All my love for you is used up. If you ever come before me again, that day will be your last.'

That was how Moses got back to Pithom. If, in Pharaoh's eyes, it was symbolically just to send him there, it was politically ridiculous. Most of the Israeli Hapirus were delighted to see him. His message echoed the memories of their tribe, gave them back their pride, made it very hard for the Pithom officials to control them.

The Egyptians who lived in Pithom town had already, against the government's orders, tried to buy the god of the Israelis off with jewellery and cash. They would stop even the quietest slaves in the street and say, 'Tell your god that the Egyptian Deniva (or whatever the Egyptian's name *was*) has offered something so that his family will be safe.'

These valuables were supposed to go into a tribal treasury run by men like Caleb and Joshua. For the tribe, they were sure, would soon have a separate existence, and would need money to pay its way.

In the same way, the Israeli Hapiru had got some excellent livestock. Though Pithom city itself had suffered very little in the plagues, the citizens – like all Egypt's citizens – felt shaken. Slaves with strong personalities, the Miriam type say, might move from door to door extorting gifts. Luckily for them, the Egyptians now feared them more than they resented them.

Then, to Moses either asleep or awake, came the crucial message of the god *Who Is*. Moses went to the commissioner of Pithom with it. It was: 'One midnight I will make my way through the midst of Egypt, and first-born things in the land of Egypt will die, whether it is the first-born of Pharaoh where he sits on his throne, or the first-born of the slave woman working at the mill. All the first-born too of your cattle. All over the land of Egypt there will be loud lament. Where the Israelis dwell, all will be quiet, man and beast, not a dog will howl. You will know at last how great a difference the god *Who Is* makes between Egypt and Israel.'

'I have to go,' said Moses, when the message had been delivered, 'to tell all this to Pharaoh.'

The commissioner said, 'I have orders from Merneptah himself not to let you go near him, no matter what you say. He says that you will say anything to get attention.'

'Perhaps you should write to him and ask him.'

In a way, you couldn't blame the commissioner for getting angry. 'The deaths you threaten us with, strutting up and down, telling us ridiculous things. If I had the authority, you would be dead.'

Moses found himself yet again under house arrest, this time in Pithom. Just the same the commissioner must have written to Pharaoh. After two days the commissioner visited Moses in the small room where the prisoner had been kept. 'He doesn't want to see you. He said that sacrifices are being made to Egypt's gods for the sake of his son. For the sake of other sons. For the sake of cattle. He says his physicians guarantee him the life of his son, the way they guaranteed the return of clear water to the river, an end to flies, frogs, hail and locusts. He says I am to return you to the slaves.'

When he was let go, Moses went back to the camp. Through the tribal organisation that had grown up in Pithom since he had returned from the desert, he sent the message. Each family was to sacrifice a male yearling lamb or a male yearling kid. The sacrifice was to be ritual, dedicated to the

OVERLEAF 'That night the meat was to be roasted over the fire, eaten with quickly prepared bread that hadn't had time to ferment'

god *Who Is*. When the lamb or kid had been slaughtered according to the tribal custom, some of its blood was to be sprinkled on the doorway, on both the jambs and the lintel of the house in which the lamb or kid was to be eaten. That night the meat was to be roasted over the fire, eaten with quickly prepared bread that hadn't had time to ferment. Nothing else was to be eaten with the meat except wild herbs. Everything of the animal was to be roasted and eaten; head, feet, entrails. Whatever was left over was to be burnt in the fire. The families were to dine in this way fully dressed, ready to travel.

A terrible message like that – you can't disobey it. *I*, and you know what I am, *I* wouldn't ignore it. Neither did any of the people like Dathan, who had wanted to get on in a friendly way with Egypt, ignore it.

What happened that night? It is hard for anyone who wasn't there to know. The Hapiru slaves of Pithom, indoors, stark-eyed, blood on their doors for the god *Who Is* to see. The blood of their obedience. The legends say that all the first-born children in Egypt died that night. I can't help thinking there's something wrong with people who can feel happy about that. Anyhow, many people did die. Amongst them Pharaoh's sickly son – a child whom Moses would always mourn. 'His father forfeited him,' Moses would say. 'Forfeited his own boy.'

No Hapiru died that night in Pithom, but the Egyptians of Pithom city suffered deaths. All morning, as the camp lay under the rare smell of roasted meat, wailers – both sincere and hired – could be heard from all over the city.

The commissioner rode out to the outskirts of the camp. 'I want to see that man. You know which one.'

When Moses came he was impressed by the force of grief in the commissioner.

'I told him,' Moses said, 'he was told many times. A deaf king is a terrible disease for all his people.'

The commissioner said, 'I have no authority to punish you yet. I could invent a voice that said "Hang him in scaffolding from chains high in the sun, for as many days as it takes to burn the life out of him." But you see, I have a just mandate from my king Pharaoh. I do not exceed it.'

'No one denies,' said Moses, the Hapiru slave, 'that you exercise your power justly, within its limits.'

'I do not expect compliments from the butt-end of camels, nor from you. My task for today is to prevent the free population of Pithom from rampaging through the camp. Tell your god who gives our young lockjaw and a fever, that I am protecting his people for the moment. When an extermination order from the gracious Merneptah arrives, I shall joyfully put it in force.'

'Anyhow, many people did die. Amongst
them Pharaoh's sickly son'

The Lawgiver and the bloody River

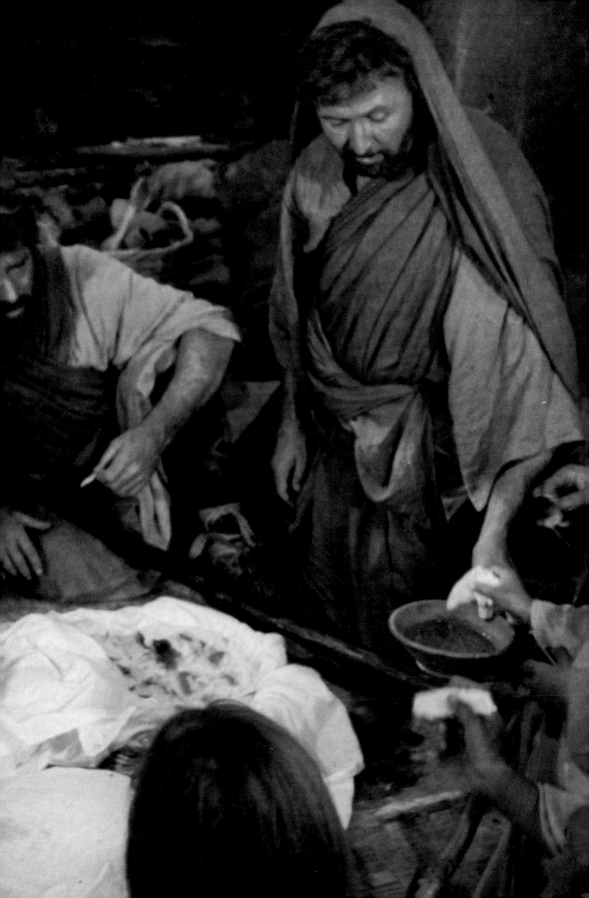

As he was turning his horse to ride away, he remembered something. 'Tell all your bloody Hapiru to fetch their dough from the public bakeries. They won't eat Egypt's good bread any more. See it done.'

All that morning Israeli women visited the bakery and carried away their dough in kneading-troughs on their shoulders. It gave them a strange elation; for at least two generations, probably three or four, they had had their bread baked for them by Egyptians. Now they were to be entirely their own bakers.

Dathan found Moses in the communal courtyard by Miriam's barracks. 'What do the Hapiru do now for bread?'

'Any free man can learn the uses of yeast.'

'You have made any solution but your own impossible. If *I* walked through the city, they would either spit at me, beat me up, or offer me jewellery so that I would take myself and my disastrous god into the desert. It would be useless for me to say, I respect law and order, I respect the Egyptian way.'

'The Egyptian way is to put a man over you with a length of rope in his hand. Do you respect that?'

'I don't expect the impossible. I am happy with a world that works at all. And yet here are people begging me to leave the sane world and go to the desert you desire. Well I tell you, I desire no desert.'

'There is a land promised.'

'Rubbish.'

The Lawgiver takes his People out of Pithom

For two days the commissioner of Pithom kept the Egyptians in the city and the Hapiru in the camp. No work or business was done, except by skilled morticians in the city. Moses spent the two days organising an order of evacuation. At the same time Dathan's group sent a testimonial of loyalty to the commissioner inside Pithom camp. They were sure that there would soon be a slaughter and wanted to be exempt from it.

And then Merneptah's order arrived. The Israeli Hapiru were to go and never be seen in Egypt again. They were not to be molested, but to take live-stock and whatever else was theirs with them. 'If they owe money, if they have extorted anything, I want that forgotten. The injustice doesn't count as much as my desire to have them out of my boundaries as instantly as it can be arranged.'

The commissioner posted this order one midday. One can only guess what he thought of it. Perhaps he, like Pharaoh, was sure that something dreadful would happen to them in the desert. In some ways they were right.

By the next noon the camp was empty. All the twelve clans, the willing and the unwilling, were on the road to Succoth. The Israelis never forget to celebrate these days. They call the feast Pesach, or Passover.

Yet from the beginning of their march they began to behave badly. There were arguments about work rosters and food rationing. Just as you'd expect from a tribe who had been getting their food and bread and water handed to them by another race.

In fact they were moving towards me. Not that the day of our meeting would be much remembered by the tribe. But even by then, after a long time in the wasteland, controlling the tribe, controlling its memory of Egypt, was still the greatest struggle Prince Moses had.

Each clan had its hereditary leaders, most of them used to being pleasant to the Egyptians. The true leaders were the little cells of men and women who had always supped on the idea of a future for Israel, either as a tribe or nation. In the early days of the march these men and women had no official power. They could not decide themselves on how the rationing was to be done, on what the punishments were to be for stealing cattle or food or water.

There were also men amongst the clans who had always done the sacrifices,

'Was there any place in the lakes, he wondered, where people could wade across?'

OVERLEAF 'Some people rushed off across the sandpit, into the wind which kept the tide down'

acting as priests. They too had some moral influence amongst these people who yesterday had been settled slaves and now were desert nomads. Many of them, and it would always be this way, moaned as much as any other tribesmen.

Without Moses, the only tribal member who knew the desert, the most unrelenting man amongst them, Merneptah's idea would have worked out. They would have all died in Sinai and have deserved to. The god *Who Is* would have to look for another tribe to nurse along.

There was the question of enforcing basic law. Aaron, Moses, Joshua the young rebel, spoke of it during the first two evenings of the tribe's escape. For in the evenings the tribal leaders would get reports of quarrels over livestock, about ex-foremen who still wanted to use their muscle, about the misuse of food and the hoarding of jewellery. In the prison camps they had always referred these grievances to Egyptian magistrates. Now they referred them to Moses.

Aaron thought there ought to be a court to deal with crimes and mis-demeanours. Its chief judge should be his brother. Such a court should please the god *Who Is*, because it would help keep his bride-race clear of blemishes.

Joshua said, 'The Egyptians have courts. They behave properly for fear of their courts. We ought to have something better. *We* – the active ones – we ought to act and speak so much and in such a way that any Israeli would be ashamed not to act and speak like us.'

He was an idealist at that stage, you see. Aaron was not slow to point it out to him.

'Police forces, courts,' the young man persisted. 'They are different from an army. An army is a weapon against strangers. Courts and police are a weapon against one's own flesh. We should have an army, but not the other.'

'We ought to,' Moses said, to end the argument, 'test what the young man is saying. As a compliment to our brothers. It is no use beginning a journey like this mistrusting each other.'

'Later?' Aaron asked.

'We'll see how they behave.'

There was a more important question at the moment. Moses wondered where to cross the lakes between Egypt and the wasteland. He was making for the Lake Timsah, for the ferry. But it would take at least a week to ferry the tribe across. There was risk in that. The tribe would be idle, half on one side of the vast lake, half on the other. There would be a lot of drinking and womanising. Men who thought the way Dathan did would go round whispering things that would only lead to unrest. There was also this danger: Pharaoh might send the army after them.

Was there any place in the lakes, he wondered, where people could wade across? He was sure that once he had them over, in the Wilderness of Shur, he could hold them.

He sent a message down the column: Anyone who knew a place on the lakes where many people could cross at once, even wading, was to come and speak to him. Only one man presented himself. He had been a wagoner in Pi-Rameses and had often driven cartloads of a special tiling clay from the shores of the Sea of Reeds near Baalzephon in the north. At low tide a sand bar was revealed. Sometimes it was only ankle-deep all the way across, at others completely dry. Some of the locals often crossed, a lake on either side of them. How long did it take to cross? Three hours, taking your time.

Moses still wondered. Two days march north to the Reed Sea, a wait for low tide, half a day to cross, two more days march south on the far side of the crossing. That would be more than four days that their column would be side-on to Egypt. Just the same, it was better than waiting a week or more at Timsah ferry.

He questioned the wagoner three times. The man seemed reliable.

'Are you sure the sand bank hasn't been washed away?'

'I am not, lord. But it has been there. Ever since I first started carting faience clay from the lake.'

And in some dream inhabited by the god *Who Is*, Moses heard the order

given. He was to go that way. Not only would the tribe cross but it would see there a great defeat of Merneptah. So they did a hard march two days north, very exhausting for couples with small children and for old people.

They crossed the highway called the Way of the Land of the Philistines. If followed it would have taken them straight up to the sweet coast of Palestine. But there were Egyptian garrisons all the way, and Horeb, the mountain he had orders to take the tribe to, was not in that direction. Just the same, there were a lot of loud men in the column who wanted to take the road. Amateur soldiers, they talked about the military peril of marching like this, with their left side in the direction of Pi-Rameses.

Just after sunset on the second day the wagoner led Moses down the beach of the Sea of Reeds and pointed to the unbroken water. 'There is the sand-bar. It's high tide now, of course.'

Yet you could see nothing ahead but water. Moses had to suppress anger against the wagoner. Yet it is my decision, he thought. Mine and that of *He Who Is*.

The annoying Dathan, who kept at the front of the column if he could, all the better to snipe at the leadership's decisions, made remarks about the excellent opportunity the lake afforded for a dry crossing. 'Anyone seven foot high would be able to cross without getting wet above the ears.'

That night, people straggled in till very late. Yet there was a great veil of light in the sky. They pointed to it, it was Yahweh giving them heart on their long walk. That veil of light in the sky was to become part of the tribe's memory. So too a whirlwind you'll hear about in a second.

Moses spent the night on the beach. The wagoner slept, but not the leader of the Hapirus. In the small hours, as the tide went out, he went wading. There was a sand-bar. He walked a long way with the water up to his knees. By the time he got back to shore the water had dropped even more. Soon after dawn a muddy bank of reddish sand stood before them, stretching across towards the desert, the lake waters divided on either side of it. Across in Sinai a great whirlwind, high as the sky, funnelled the desert sand up. A wind blew from that direction, suppressing the tide, baring the sand-bank more and more.

As far as the tribe was concerned it was *He Who Is* manifested in the whirlwind, just as in the veils of fire the night before. People waiting with pains in their muscles saw it and felt better.

A great tribal enthusiasm swept over the shores of the Reed Sea. That awesome funnel of cloud and sand would do wonderful things for them today. Moses went amongst people saying, 'Over there, we won't have to march so fast. Desert people never exhaust themselves.'

The young tribesmen who camped at the rear of the column, some of them already carrying arms in case of meeting hostile tribes in Sinai, came running up to the shore. One of them who had gone a little westward the night before had thought he could see camp-fires. Now there were clouds of dust, as from the hooves of many horses, in the direction of Baalzephon. They were frightened, and the fright spread through the tribe.

No one amongst the Israelis ever found out what the purpose of that pursuing Egyptian army was.

On the morning itself, Moses' supporters went about telling everyone it was coming to exterminate the tribe. It's more likely that Merneptah, recovered from his Moses madness and – to an extent – from the death of his boy, had now begun to act in an Egyptian manner. With that amazing cool-headed justice the Egyptians can show, he probably meant simply to return the slaves to the wholeness of the Egyptian State. After, of course, trying and condemning the leaders of the revolt.

But at the edge of the Reed Sea, amongst the dust and braying of animals and the wailing of children, no one was very philosophic about Merneptah's intentions. Some people rushed off across the sand-spit, into the wind which kept the tide down. But others sat down on their bed-rolls in the sun to wait for the army. Panic had dazed them.

Moses and his allies went round talking people into moving towards the sand-bank. On the low ridges to the east you could see dust now, and sun on metal.

A lot of people just stood aside. They wanted to spend their last hours throwing sand at members of Moses' party and making bitter speeches.

'Weren't there enough graves for us in Egypt? That you had to bring us out here to die? What sort of thing was it in the first place, to bring us away from Egypt? Didn't we all tell you while we were still there, damn it all? We said, leave us to the Egyptian way . . .'

Moses kept saying, 'You won't be touched. The god *Who Is* intends you won't be touched.'

'*His intentions!* What about the intentions of bloody Merneptah?'

'For one thing, they can't take chariots out along a sand-bar . . .'

'They just put on more horses. Didn't you know? They've got limitless horses.'

'Before they can cross, high tide will come in.'

But even the wagoner at his elbow denied this. 'With this wind, even high tide won't cover the bar.'

'Then the wind will change.'

'How do you know?' an Israeli asked. 'All we know is, it's a matter of

dying in comfort here or running all morning and dying exhausted over there.'

But as the dust in the east billowed more and you could see more clearly the sun on the copper hats of Merneptah's army, everyone moved onto the spit and began walking. In fact, Joshua's group had to stop them trampling old people into the sand. As they went, women and men cried and keened. They cursed the spiral of wind which could still be seen over in Sinai. They knew what it was: a tall symbol of the desert god who had seduced them to this bitter lake.

I myself have got every sympathy for them. If I'd been there I'd have bad-mouthed everyone. In between rehearsing some likely story to give Merneptah's infantry.

The Israelis knew two things about that day. First, that Merneptah was with his army. His was a staff tent on the low hills a mile from the lake. The distance one could see was practically unlimited at dawn but getting less now, as the fierce wind from Sinai mounted. Grit got in the royal eye that morning.

Secondly, it was believed that he had the whole army of Egypt out that day, that he'd called in divisions from Busiris and from beyond the First Cataract!

But even if he wanted to exterminate the tribe, two or (at most) three divisions would have done for a quick job. You see, three divisions would have meant five soldiers for every tribesman, or more significantly, six hundred chariots to ride the tribe down.

BELOW 'The Israelis knew two things about
that day. First, that Merneptah was with
his army'

I can understand why the story grew that the whole army of Egypt was at the Reed Sea that day. If you were a tribesman with a wife limp from hysteria and two young children, and looked back and saw the mounted scouts of the Tanis Re division cantering on the beach, waiting for the chariots to come up, and if you could see the dust of at least five hundred chariots, then *you'd* probably think Merneptah had called out his whole damn army.

I mention the Tanis Re because Moses once told me that after the events some wooden regimental plaques of that division were washed ashore in Sinai.

To return to the panic on the sand-bar. The whirlwind, since called 'The Pillar of the Cloud' by Hapiru myth-makers, had begun to shift subtly and then with speed. The wind moved round to the north quite suddenly, about three hours after dawn. The Israelis still on the sand-bar saw waves kicking up to their left, not enough to alarm them any more than they were already.

Perhaps the Egyptian general thought the wind would hang off in that north-east direction long enough for his troops to make a journey across the bar. Why shouldn't it? Then, if the army got stranded on the far side, they could be ferried back.

The last of the tribesmen were nearly across when the general decided his

mounted scouts and his chariots should go after them. The infantry could follow the chariots.

Because they were worn out, the Israelis rested now in Sinai. From narrow eyes and nearly silent, they watched scouts, then chariots, then infantry regiments advance out onto the sand-bar. If someone asked 'Why don't they bog?' I'm sure someone else would have answered, 'The Egyptians know how to build wheels that don't bog.' Because even now, forty years later, the tribe of Israel still has great respect for Egyptian science.

Still, on the morning, it was slow enough going and hard work for the charioteers and the horses.

Joshua sought Moses. 'If we drive our livestock head on for them it will confuse them. And slow the chariots.'

'It doesn't matter,' said Moses. 'The wind will change.'

'Do you know that?'

Moses began to yell so that he could be widely heard. 'See those regiments. You're seeing them for the last time. The wind will change.'

People wailed and screamed, wishing it would happen.

When the leading scouts were only half a mile away, many of the tribesmen straggled inland. But after a while, they had to sit down again. As yet they did not have the knowledge or the breathing habits of a desert traveller.

Scouts were now a few stone-throws from shore. 'Yahweh, when?' Moses screamed, trampling amongst his recumbent and wailing tribe. 'When? When?'

Then, as everyone knows, the wind and whirlwind went fair around to the north and blew madly. The waves built up in the Sea of Reeds. Instantly they grew six feet high, beating on the bar, breaking over it. In seconds, chariots were axle deep, The army waded. Wheels bogged now, beyond the powers of the chariot horses. The wind grew more, bringing the tide in higher, further.

You can imagine why this would become a song to the tribe. The unanswerable army of the Nineteenth Dynasty, infantry, armour, engineers, service units all moving in order towards an easy objective, adequate and reasonable tools in their hands. And then the wind changes and they begin to wade. And the wind grows and they become individual men, panicking and weighed down. And there is yelling and the season's highest water comes over the bar and undermines it at the same time. Men of two divisions have little purchase at all on the sand beneath, and then the sand is gone. At least ten thousand men are roaring in the Sea of Reeds, but not for long. Their equipment takes them down, and they come up only when they are drowned and bloated in their uniforms.

The Lawgiver and the
poor Travellers

That day was a rest day and the bodies washed onto the east shore were buried.

In the evening a song began to be sung:

> *Vain the chariot, vain the horsemen.*
> *I will teach the Egyptians to know me, Elohim,*
> *For what I am.*

There was awe and talking. 'Even though we were running, we didn't throw anything away. We didn't throw away flour or silver. We didn't throw away pots and pans. We didn't throw away tents. We didn't try to leave our slow-footed animals. Why?' It was the truth, they had come into the desert fairly well equipped. Yahweh, they were sure, had not let them throw anything away.

There was also drinking and good dancing, girls dancing. And dalliance by way of celebration. They were not sure yet precisely what Elohim wanted of them by way of behaviour. And even when they were, they weren't all that strait-laced.

'In the morning,' Moses said by his fire, 'they'll understand they have their freedom. And are in the desert.'

There were some tribal leaders with him drinking palm wine. Even that had not been thrown away. One of the leaders said, 'Best not to paint too dark a picture.'

'No, let them know it. Free people have to know what's ahead of them. They have to plan for their needs. Especially over here, where there's so little. Slaves have the luxury of having things provided. We aren't slaves any longer.'

'Eheu!' said a tribal leader. It was a grunt and there was already regret in it, for the old days that had ended only last week.

Meanwhile, Miriam, a tambourine in her hands, was dancing.

> *That power* [she sang] *could hurl the king's army,*
> *the king's chariots, into the sea.*
> *Drowned in the Reed Sea*
> *the flower of his chivalry.*

'Meanwhile, Miriam, a tambourine in her
hands, was dancing'

The depths have closed them over,
they went down to the bottom like rocks . . . .
the hot breath of your anger burned them up like stubble.
The blast of your anger heaped the waters up.
Then waves were still.
And at the sea's heart,
the depths congealed . . .

When Moses went to relieve himself in the dark he tripped over a boy and
a girl. He felt peevish and shooed them away to some other corner of the
night. That's it, he thought, I want Zipporah.

The desert was not only hard for them. They had no tribe-memory of it.
So they behaved badly.

First, there were gangs who extorted water and food from old people.
In a true tribe, there are customs and punishments to stop this sort of thing
happening. The Israeli Hapiru were a tribe only in name. What they were in
fact was the rabble of slum dwellers.

Reports of brawls and beatings-up and half-murders came in each evening. And some women were attracting payments in food and water by acting as harlots.

Practically speaking, the Israelis were hopeless. Sheep wandered so often, and the families who owned them staggered off after them. Stopping people from getting lost, stopping the whole tribe from breaking up daily into two dozen bewildered little groups was, for Moses, the business of the day.

Lacking water, those who got any sort of fever died. Their relatives came wailing round the camp carrying the corpses, screaming, *This man or woman or child wouldn't have died in Egypt*. Which was only the truth.

Moses kept promising them a place called Mara, where there was water. When they reached it, they found a few palms and straggly acacias and a bitter spring running down from a rock behind the trees. The first people who tasted the water wailed (in character!) and said it was too bitter. Moses cut down one of the palms near by – it was of the aromatic kind – and hurled it into the spring. Somehow it made the water more drinkable. So, though there was some dysentery, there was now water for it.

At Mara, after everyone had rested, he gave them the beginnings of the tribal laws. All the excesses of the first week's march in Sinai were now outlawed. Beatings-up, thieving of water, harlotry would never again be so freely practised in that tribe.

It didn't stop them moaning about their food. They were still eating girdle cakes made from the unfermented dough that they had carried away from the Egyptian bakeries near Pithom.

Now they had a hard walk from Mara to Elim. On that stretch, every Israeli with any sense began to learn how to ration his food, his water, even his breathing and bodily movements. How Prince Moses kept them together during those few months, I don't quite understand. Although they talked about going back to Egypt, perhaps they still had a dread of that king who had sent an army after them. They also understood that they had to stay with Moses because he was the only one who knew the desert, who could make water drinkable with a tree trunk and find food in the crevices of rocks.

Elim was a better place than Mara when they got there. The water had no alkali in it. There were dozens of date palms. They rested there and were not bothered by any other tribes. Perhaps they were too numerous for that. Many of them wanted to stay there, but that little oasis wasn't meant to keep so many people. The water began to foul. And Moses went round saying that after they had sacrificed to the god *Who Is* on Horeb, they would be given a suitable land, whose waters would not run foul.

Turning inland to avoid the mines, they camped one evening just as the

'Now they had a hard walk from Mara to Elim'

OVERLEAF 'Moses told each head-of-family he could collect up to four pints of this manna each morning that it lay on the ground'

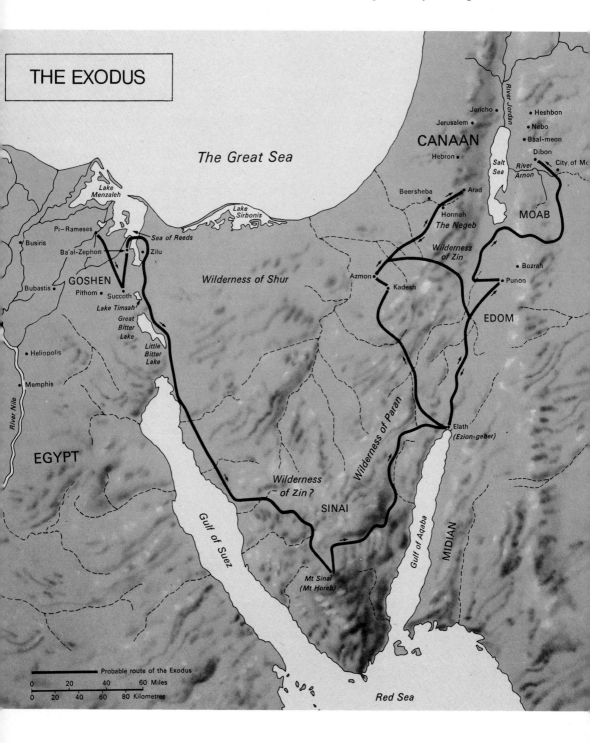

THE EXODUS

The Great Sea

CANAAN

Jericho
Jerusalem
Heshbon
Nebo
Baal-meon
Hebron
Dibon
City of Mo
Salt
Sea
River
Arnon

Lake
Menzaleh
Lake
Sirbonis

Beersheba
Arad
MOAB

Pi-Rameses
Sea of Reeds
Hormah
The Negeb

Busiris
Ba'al-Zephon
Zilu
Wilderness
of Zin

GOSHEN
Pithom
Succoth
Wilderness of Shur
Azmon
Kadesh
Bozrah
Punon

Bubastis

Lake Timsah
Great
Bitter
Lake
EDOM

Heliopolis
Little
Bitter
Lake

Memphis

Wilderness of Paran

Elath
(Ezion-geber)

EGYPT

Wilderness
of Zin ?

SINAI
Gulf of Suez
Gulf of Aqaba
MIDIAN

Mt Sinai
(Mt Horeb)

Probable route of the Exodus

0   20   40   60 Miles
0   20   40   60   80 Kilometres

Red Sea

sky filled with circling quail. The birds landed all about. They had flown out of Africa and were exhausted. So that all the tribesmen had to do was walk amongst them wringing their necks. They also threw up nets to snare them. They gutted them and put them in the sun to dry out. Likewise where tamarisk trees dropped their resin overnight, the tribe was allowed to pick it up and feed their families with it. When they could get it, they always ate it – it became the tribal food. As the song says it was white and flaky and

> *looked like coriander seed;*
> *its taste was like that of flour mixed with honey.*

It was tiresome food, but it kept them alive.

Trying to make them more tribal, Moses told each head-of-family he could collect up to four pints of this manna each morning that it lay on the ground. Only on the sixth day were they supposed to collect enough for two days. There was a practical reason for stopping them collecting too much. The stuff went maggoty after a day or two.

After the quail incident, and after the manna began to be eaten, an argument developed between Miriam and Aaron.

'They're so weak-minded from slavery,' Miriam said. 'They think the quail and the manna are miracles.'

Aaron said, 'You can't deny it's amazing. That the quail should come down in such numbers.'

'Moses lets people think it's a matter of miracles so he can control the tribe better. That's a fair reason. But you? You just enjoy being a magician.'

'I enjoy my task now,' Aaron admitted, 'better than I did when I was a slave. I admit that to you.'

'In your present tasks, it's dangerous to enjoy. Yahweh does not act for your enjoyment.'

'I know. I am just a human tool.'

'I can remember when you detested him.'

'Elohim?'

'Your brother Moses.'

'I love Elohim and my brother Moses.'

'Loving your brother Moses is a change. Don't forget our late mother left you to wet-nurse him.'

'That's all finished, that old business.'

But Miriam went on seeing dangers in Aaron's small-time pride.

It was about this time, when they were living off dried quail and small supplies of manna, that they acquired me in the way I earlier told you.

After capture, I was kept in a tent for some days. Some of Joshua's young men slept in the same tent. They knew in any case I could not leave them. In a wilderness I could get nowhere without a camel, a guide, skins of water. My future was already decided. Unless we met up with an Egyptian garrison, I was to be a tribesman.

It was incredible really. The whole tribe was living off a trickle of poor water that flowed out of an outcrop of limestone close to where I was taken. As the history of the tribe will show you, limestone is very good for holding water. But such a trickle can give out at any second. One evening, when I was asked to eat with the Representative, the leader, I mentioned it to him. Tentatively, in case he turned nasty.

He said, 'The god *Who Is* didn't bring his bride-race all this way to kill them off here.'

'In my experience,' I dared to say, 'gods can behave in very back-handed ways.'

'I admit,' he replied, 'that in the normal way of things, a trickle from limestone can finish without warning. I admit that thereby a whole tribe could go mad and die. I simply have guarantees that it won't happen to this tribe.'

I was somehow annoyed by the man. 'Don't you ever have doubts?' I asked him.

'Yes. But not nearly enough to make life comfortable.'

Some of those valleys up in the mountains of Zin have quite a few tamarisks. There is always water there if you have an eye for it. In a high valley, I saw the further growth of Moses' law. He was obsessed with the idea that the tribesmen should rest one day of the week, the way Yahweh had rested when making the earth. A lot of tribesmen thought this meant they rested from marching. But no, he wanted them to rest absolutely, not moving at all in the daylight. I was near by when Joshua's young guards brought to Moses' tent some families who had been caught gathering the floury resin of the tamarisk trees off the ground during the rest day. The brother, Aaron, was called in and made a speech and sentenced the families to a day's fasting.

As his sister Miriam did, I too found something suspicious in Aaron's speech and the way he spread his arms. And when the culprits bowed to him, he seemed to inflate, like a pleased cat.

Another time, I saw an old husband dragging his young wife towards the leader's tent. Behind them, half angry, half protective, half hanging back, walked a young man, obviously the wife's lover. They entered Moses' tent. Aaron walked from his own tent to his brother's, waiting at the flap, expecting to be called in. He was not. He listened to his brother questioning the people. In fact, Moses' weirdly subdued, stammering, Egyptian style of anger confused people.

When the people left the tent, the wife and the lover were sobbing. The lover went to move off in a different direction from the wife and husband. Aaron detained them all. He couldn't stop himself making a speech of his own.

'As my brother said,' he told them, 'this sort of thing is a threat to the tribe and therefore an insult to Yahweh. The day will soon come when the guilty will have their throats cut like sheep.'

Moses came to the tent door. 'Let them go brother. I have done all I will do to them. Now we wait.'

The young man turned to both brothers. 'And a young wife with an old husband. She waits too. She waits for a lover. And that won't be changed.'

The Lawgiver's desert Victories

What the tribe was making for now was the well at Rephidim. I tried not to think what might happen if the well were empty. It was late summer when we came down into the valley, the rains had not started. The well *was* exhausted.

The tribe had three- or four-days' short ration of water left. They made their normal speeches and screeches. They were too far out in the wasteland for a return to Egypt to be a real possibility. But they still complained and compared all the time. I was amazed. Listening to them, you would have thought they'd been businessmen, cabinet ministers, physicians in Egypt. Not forced labour. Moses came to me where I was pitching tent for Joshua. In fact, *I* was forced labour now, but had not yet complained about it to Moses.

When he came up he stood and prayed in front of me at first.

He said, loudly but still with that weird Egyptian restraint in his voice, 'Yahweh, soon they will start stoning me.' Then to me he said, 'Are you good at finding limestone?'

'The sort that has caves and sinkholes?' I suggested.

'Yes, I don't want chalk. I want rock that will hold water.'

'You will have to let me have the tools I had when I was captured.'

So I was given back the hammers and chisels and bars I had had with me on the day I was captured. We left the camp. People threw dust at our backs and invited us to get lost in the hills. Moses smiled slightly.

'Up and down, up and down,' he said. 'That's them.'

He was more certain than I was that we would find a limestone outcrop. Therefore, when it presented itself high up to one side of the valley, I very nearly missed it.

'What about that up there?' Moses suggested. And there it was, exactly the sort of blue-grey limestone he wanted.

It took us half a day to reach it, climb it, and explore the sink holes on top of it. By dropping stones in we found the holes were full of deep water. Sweet limestone water. Centuries of rain caught and held there. Then I tested the front of the cliff. A few blows with a mallet caused water to leak out of the rock. We drank it and then sealed the gap with clay.

One good blow here,' I said. 'And the water will flow.'

'We must move the people up first. It is not to be wasted.'

So the people were brought up the valley, and Moses hit the rock with his staff, and the sweet water flowed out. And when everyone had drunk enough and was feeling rosy again, the hole was stopped with clay. For they were getting wiser now, more canny in dealing with the goods the desert and Yahweh gave them.

When people hear me tell this story, they say, 'He wasn't an ungrateful man. Why did he never admit that a Cretan miner found the water for him?'

I can only answer, to him there was only one finder, Yahweh. And Yahweh provided me and the leader with that outcrop.

There, at Rephidim, I met a girl called Joannah. She was about eighteen, had no children, only a husband about my age. The husband's name was Naom.

We had dug a dam so that water could be released from the limestone to make a pool. The pool was lined with clay, branches, stones, to stop the water seeping away. Here people would come to water their sheep and goats. One evening, while I was on top of the rock, testing the depth of water in the sink holes, I saw the girl coming. She was barefooted, yet her feet looked delicate. Her face was broad. She was laughing with the boy who helped her with the flock. It turned out to be her young brother. She had a tall throat, and round it a bead necklace. She took the breath out of my mouth. She had the look of a virgin, so I called out, 'Woman, whose daughter are you?'

She laughed. 'My father would have nothing to say to you,' she shouted back. 'I am wife of a man called Naom in the Judah clan.'

'You make me very sad then,' I called. It was the truth.

I next met her more sadly. There are desert people called Amalekites. They are not as pleasant as the *bedu*. They are a fly-blown and nasty race. One evening a clan of them came down from the hills. It was a quick raid. In less than a few minutes they had killed a number of Israeli herders, and were driving part of the tribe's flocks away. One of the shepherds killed was Joannah's brother. I saw her the next day in the funeral procession. They sang the weird old funeral chants they'd brought out of the desert into Egypt with them and now had taken out of Egypt back into the desert. I wanted to go up and touch her face, on which there were tears. But in an Israeli funeral procession, the men have one place, and the women another.

When I woke up the next morning I found there had been another raid. The tribe, even the bereaved, did not talk so much now. There was a profound anger in them. Everyone seemed to be making crude bows out of the branches of the tamarisks and, at a fire in the middle of the camp, black-

smiths were melting metals – cauldrons, ornaments, picks – down into sharp-edged weapons.

In the evening, when I was up at the limestone cliffs, I saw her coming again with her sheep. She was alone. A little down the hill was a group of Joshua's armed young men. Not close enough to inhibit me.

I went up to her. 'I was very sorry at your loss, Joannah,' I said. She did not look at me but the tears came down her cheeks. I put my hand against her jaw as if to catch them. At this tenderness, she began to cry even more. Old Naom wasn't a very attentive or gentle husband, as it turned out.

She said, 'I am so tired.'

'There is a resting-place, around the outcrop. So cool.'

I led her there and behaved gently. That's how we became lovers.

Meanwhile, the Amalekites were so happy with their earlier raids that they got as much of their tribe together as they could. It might have been only five hundred men they gathered, or perhaps a thousand at the outside. But they were armed and used to raiding.

One morning they appeared in a long line along the top of the valley. No one in the Israeli camp had fought in a battle before, but they were more or

'There are desert people called Amalekites . . .
one evening a clan of them came down from
the hills. It was a quick raid'

The Lawgiver's desert Victories

less willing to follow Joshua's instructions. First, women and children and old people were to sit down in their tents under the ridge where the limestone wells lay. In front of them were to stand young boys with sling-shots and piles of stones. In front of them, archers. And either side of the archers, on high ground, Joshua's young men with metal-tipped javelins and brittle swords.

'They need more than they have,' said Moses.

He told them aloud, 'I will stand on that hill there. I will hold up my arms. While my arms are up, you will know that the battle is going your way.'

He knew that by standing on a ridge in this way, he would be a standing symbol. His raised arms would help hold back hysteria.

But the comedy of it was that by the time we got on top of the hill, having brought no water, we were quite exhausted. As the Amalekites rode down off their hill into the valley, Moses knew that to stand in the sun for hours, without water, his arms upheld, would be no easy matter.

'You rest, Aaron, and you, Hur.' (Hur was the name they called me, being unable to pronounce my Cretan name.) 'If I get faint, you'll have to hold me up.'

The Amalekites, some on camels, some on scraggy horses, some on donkeys, came down the valley three times. The first time the unexpected hail of arrows surprised them. Not that they left many dead. But you could hear the Israelis laughing below us, and Moses, hands outstretched, laughing in a strange way too.

The second charge exhausted all the arrows, and the Amalekites kept coming. It was at moments like that that the Israelis looked up to see if the leader's arms were still upheld. The archers withdrew to the line where the boys with stones were. Joshua's young men took the mounted enemy from the sides. It was a short, bloody session that was now fought out. The Israelis captured many animals and the weapons of the dead.

For the rest of the day the Amalekites kept out of sight.

'We have to go down and get water for you,' Aaron told his brother. I was delighted to hear this news.

'No, I came up here to sustain them. I can't go down to them and ask for water.'

It was terrible up there. We could scarcely speak. We pulled our head-cloths down over our eyes. The breath we took in was scalding, and when we breathed out, our nostrils seemed to burn.

'I don't think they will trouble your tribe again.'

'All the desert peoples know the Amalekites. They will trouble us.'

And in the late afternoon, they came again from two directions. There was a tremendous hand to hand brawl. You could hear young Israelis screaming when they were hurt. They had not expected to be soldiers or, worse still, wounded soldiers.

Aaron, Moses and I on our hilltop were delirious for water. 'Hold me up,' Moses said. 'And my arms.' We obeyed him. It was like placing struts to keep a tree up.

I don't doubt that seeing him made a difference to the performance of the men below us.

A second time the Amalekites ran away. Women came out of the Israeli camp, looking for the bodies of their men. If they found them, and found they had died of wounds in the belly or on the head, they set up a terrible funeral wail. It was into this noise that we moved as we came down the mountain.

But no one threw dust at Moses this time, people stood aside for him. Joannah saw me coming and brought a water skin to me. After I had drunk, we stood together enjoying life and each other's presence. I asked her how her husband had got on that day against the Amalekites. He had been amongst the stone slingers until early afternoon, when he had been seen back to his tent for continued vomiting. The more I heard of the man, the more he seemed like me.

That night the camp was ringed with fires. The Amalekites were allowed to sneak in and take their corpses away. Not before Joshua's young men had stripped them of weapons and valuables. In the middle of the night, Moses woke calling for Joshua. When Joshua got to Moses' tent, he heard that the leader had had a dream and that in the dream the voice had said, I intend to wipe the very name of the Amalec tribe from this earth.

That is the strange thing about Yahweh. Sometimes he is like a lover, at others like a living vengeance. As Moses spoke to young Joshua that night, the idea found words; that the whole tribe of Amalec, by its ill-will towards the Hapiru tribe of Israel, had earned death.

The Lawgiver goes up the Mountain

We left Rephidim when the wounded were healed. Ahead of us was Horeb, sacred mountain of some tribes.

When next I ate with the leader, another triangle of people came to his tent. An angry husband, a weeping wife, a half-aggressive lover. Moses got strangely agitated. He stood up.

'You ought to spare me this sort of thing,' he said. As if the lover and the wife had done what they'd done just to hurt him. 'I can't work out these matters of divorce and marriage. You have children. How does one decide about children?'

When the lover began arguing, Moses went up to him, made a fist, knocked him over with a blow against the side of the head. Having done so, he screamed at the members of the triangle, 'All get out!'

Yet before they could leave, he himself went out into the night.

So he left all of us sitting fairly shamefaced at table – Aaron, Aaron's wife Elizabar, Miriam, Caleb, Joshua.

'He is worried about this Midian wife of his,' Miriam said. 'She is still young. He wonders if she's found a lover.' Then she laughed. 'I can never find a lover.'

You could see everyone at table, thinking, 'That's understandable.'

Under the ridge leading to Horeb, the big tribe of Israel met the small Midian tribe of Jethro. There were the four tents, the tents of the two brothers, Jethro's and Zipporah's tent. It turned out that the lovely wife had sat mostly indoors the whole time of her husband's absence. Her relatives, honouring her for staying chaste, brought food to her and looked after Moses' flocks along with their own.

Aaron and Miriam stood back a little aloof from their brother's family. You could see they thought Jethro's tribe looked a bit primitive. I heard Aaron say once, 'He takes a lot of notice of that hairy old man.'

That hairy old man was Jethro. And Moses *did* take notice of him.

The day after we camped at the bottom of Horeb, the old man walked amongst our encampment and found his son-in-law standing at his tent flap, listening to a line of people with petitions and complaints. Jethro sat in the

shade and watched all morning. In the early afternoon, when Moses had got rid of everyone, the old man looked up at him.

'Do you think it's clever, the way everyone comes to you?'

'The tribal leaders can do nothing to help me. They've got no authority with their people. They lost it through being slaves.'

'That's no reason to wear yourself out. Besides, if you're the one and only judge and are all the time deciding disputes between them, those who lose their case keep a grudge against you.'

'That's true.' Moses made an ironic face.

'Listen to me. Your job is to be representative of this people with the god. Your job is to refer all their affairs to him. To tell them what he wants of them. Meanwhile, you ought to choose out honest men and put them in charge of each tribe or clan, of each hundred households say, or fifty, or ten.'

'Ten?'

'You think ten is too small a group? You'd be surprised how much business and argument ten families can generate.'

'Under the ridge leading to Horeb the big
tribe of Israel met the small Midian tribe of
Jethro'

The Lawgiver goes up the Mountain

'Are there enough honest men? One for every ten families? On top of that, one for every hundred, one for every thousand?'

'If there are not, the tribe will fall to pieces. As it will if you keep on deciding every dog fight.'

I don't know why it hurt him to let go his control over every family. Maybe it was like giving up children, when you're sure they're not quite ready for the complicated world. Anyhow, it had to be done. The men were appointed, over clans, hundreds, tens. The Israelis were beginning to take on the nature as well as the name of a tribe.

Within a week Moses was very happy he had appointed tribal judges and leaders. Something happened that would have been very painful for him to deal with. You might remember there had been a night when a husband had dragged his wife and her lover to Moses' tent. The wronged husband belonged to the tribe of Judah, the lover to the tribe of Ruben. Some young men of the Judah clan who had picked up the weapons of the Amalekites off the battlefield at Rephidim, challenged the young men of Ruben to come and fight a small battle against them. Amongst the men in the Ruben clan who took up the challenge was, of course, the young lover.

The little battle, which I didn't see, took place some miles from the camp. It was very quick – the Judah boys were better armed. In any case, their purpose was to catch the young lover. They managed it, scaring the others off. One of the young Judah men cut off the genitals of the Ruben lover. Then they all went back to camp and the boy was left out there to bleed to death. Joshua arrested the young men of Judah who had done it. He was changing now. The functions of a policeman were coming naturally to him.

After the arrest he sat in Moses' tent and said, 'Is waging war inside the tribe the worst crime of all?'

'I don't know. It's bad enough.'

'I think this. I think there is only one punishment for waging war inside the tribe.'

'All right. You are a soldier. You are a judge. Perhaps you had better leave this judgment to other judges.'

The young man stood up, bowed, left without a word. Because he badly wanted to judge and condemn those young men of Judah.

In the camp under Horeb, people were saying, when will he go? Having brought them this far, when would he go up the mountain and hear from the god *Who Is* proposals for the tribe's future?

He seemed to hesitate. The rainy season came. There were violent storms on the mountain and the air in the camp seemed thin. While the storms were on and the lightning rolled, Joannah would not come near me. She was afraid she would grow ritually impure by sleeping with me. She was frightened the god on the mountain might send lightning to seek her out.

That was one of the most confusing things about living with that tribe. They all had strong ideas about what made one pure or impure. For example, a woman after childbirth was considered impure and had to undergo washings and then present herself to a priest. Likewise, men who ate certain parts of animals, touched a dead body or had a rush of seed while they slept. When they used the word *impure*, the Israeli Hapirus did not mean guilty. It just meant that they couldn't have anything to do with their god until they were clean again.

So Joannah was frightened of having anything to do with me under Horeb. For that reason, I too was anxious that Moses should go up the mountain.

At last one day when there was a rare mist on Horeb, Moses got his staff and went off. A great crowd – nearly everyone in the camp who could walk – followed him. But, at the base of the hill, he sent them back.

A lot of people waited there all day. In the evening he came back. The word went round that he could be seen on one of the lower spurs and all the tribe, except the old and nursing mothers, waited for him.

When he got to the bottom, he must have been tired. He did not sit however. I could tell that he had been an Egyptian prince – his presence, the way he walked, the crippled cadences of his voice – they were all impressive.

Moses spoke as if he were repeating something that had been said to him on the mountain. 'A message to the race of Jacob. To Israel's sons let it be known. You have seen for yourself what I did to the Egyptians, how I carried you as if you were on eagle's wings. And took you up into my care. Listen and keep your agreement with me. I, to whom the earth belongs, will single you out amongst its peoples to be my own. You will serve me as a royal priesthood, as a consecrated nation. Let the Israelis know this.'

It was amazing. The more he spoke, the more people gasped aloud, as if the message were too much for them.

When he had finished they yelled, 'Yes. We will do it.' And made other noises of assent.

I felt envious because I couldn't quite be part of their enthusiasm.

Moses spoke, and he seemed very weary. 'Then I will go back up again and tell the god *Who Is*. But I have to wait three days. In that three days, you must wash your clothes and keep yourselves clean. Husbands will have nothing to do with wives. Even more so, illicit lovers shall have nothing to

do with each other. All according to the laws of cleanliness you kept in the old times, in the desert.'

That idea didn't fill me with as much enthusiasm as it did the other members of the tribe.

On the third day, in the middle of a thunderstorm, the mountain seemed to erupt with fire. Great clouds of smoke came from the summit. It was as if the mountain had suddenly become one of those fire-breathing mountains with craters.

Now I knew that Horeb wasn't a cratered mountain. I more than any of them, being an expert. You can imagine how the fire and smoke frightened me. It was Yahweh in his guise of a living vengeance.

In the heat of the moment lovers say that nothing can separate them. I admit that that morning, when smoke and fire were on Horeb, I mentally agreed over and over to give up Joannah.

Moses camped on the mountain a number of weeks. Once he came down to warn the tribesmen not to try to climb the mountain in the naïve hope of seeing Yahweh. No one would have tried it anyhow. The mountain had just about ceased being a place on a map. When you got close to it, you felt as though the fabric of your body was about to be torn apart.

Somehow, in the midst of such force and power, Moses stayed on the mountain. Joshua camped on one of the lower spurs and carried messages between Moses and the tribe. At one stage, seventy tribal leaders and priests were invited to spend a week half way up the mountain. They went up very soberly, not having touched their wives for a week previous. Twice a day they burnt animals over fires there. They sang old songs and new, songs from the time when Yahweh's name had not been known and he was called el Shaddai and Elohim. When they came back, they told stories of having seen Yahweh as a fire on the summit.

There was no papyrus in the camp, so Moses sent down for tablets of soft stone. He intended to write on these the laws of the tribe. The writing would, it seemed, give the laws special force. Because they were written down in the presence of Yahweh's fire.

Where did this law come from, that he wrote down on the summit? The legends say it was all spoken straight out by Yahweh's voice. I hope no one will accuse me of being nasty-minded if I say it was very helpful to Moses as the law-giver to have people believe that every bit of the law he made on Horeb was spoken by Yahweh. I sometimes wonder if Yahweh would have gone to the trouble to actually say, for example, that no one should broil a kid in its mother goat's milk. I mean, doing *that* is a rite practised by Amalekites and some of the nastier desert people. When they've eaten the kid, there's some sort of orgy – homosexual. Moses had learnt to abhor the practice when he was a member of Jethro's small tribe, and he did not really need a voice on the summit to tell him to forbid it to the large tribe of the Israeli Hapirus.

Twice a day, Joshua left food for him on a spur close to the summit. It was simple food – mainly a bread and water diet. He'd insisted on that.

Life in the camp was more or less normal. Since no one had said whether I was a slave or not, I had little enough work to do now. Without Joannah there was considerable boredom. I relieved it by going out looking for minerals. One day when I was out on some ridge to the west of Horeb, I saw a movement on the slope below me. I got very worried. I thought, it's Amalekites or someone like that.

I took a firm hold on my rock hammer and started moving quickly along the ridge in the direction of the camp. Before I'd taken a hundred paces, I felt a hand on my elbow. It wasn't the hand of some desert trash. It was Dathan's hand.

'Do you like living in a tribe? In a wasteland?'

I was still trembling and wanted to hit him with my hammer for frightening me. 'It's not what I grew up to,' I said.

'None of us grew up to it.'

'You wouldn't go back.'

'What happens if we don't? We are in a desert now. We will always be in a desert. It's not a natural way to live.'

'Do you think Merneptah will want you back after what happened at the Sea of Reeds?'

'Merneptah will not hold it against us, just because the tide came in. If he punished us for that, he'd be saying our god is better than his. No, he'll see it as an unfortunate rise in the tide. It's very likely he'd treat us pretty easily, letting us settle in the grasslands.'

'Perhaps.'

'I would have thought you'd be delighted. To know that some people had the idea of going back.'

'I would have thought I'd be delighted to, too.'

'One thing about Egypt. There you don't get threatened with death just for humping your neighbour's wife. Say a man had an affair with some nice little Sarah or Joannah . . . he wouldn't be threatened with death.'

'No? It doesn't worry me in any case.'

'Pardon me. I know that's not the truth. And if I know you're involved with a woman, Moses and Yahweh will soon know too. Not that I will tell them. But this sort of news seems to spread easily.'

'You mean, you want me to support that idea? A return to Egypt? And if I don't, you'll let everyone know about Jo – the woman.'

He smiled charmingly. 'I would like you to consider that you, more than anyone, would be welcome back in Egypt. You're a person of civilised habits. So am I, to an extent. As a foreman, I used to talk familiarly with overseers, superintendants, engineers. I did not have to fight desert oafs like the Amalekites.'

'Because you were a slave.'

'In name, maybe.' Again the smile. 'I know what it is, you like *him* and you dislike me.'

'That's right.'

'Do you like him well enough to put up with years of sour water, poor food, heat blisters? I don't think so. You look to me like a man who likes his comforts.'

The way he talked, implying he knew me so well, annoyed me. 'Listen, you make your silly plans, but don't come to me with them. You don't interest me, and – I hope – I don't interest you.'

'You mean the business of Joannah? For the time being, it won't be mentioned to anyone.'

I told him that if I *ever* found him mentioning it I would break his skull with a rock hammer. I would drive a tent peg through his head while he slept. It was only when he was trudging away that I thought to ask him,

'The fire and the clouds of smoke on the summit? Didn't it mean something to you? That this is the place for your tribe?'

'He's an Egyptian,' Dathan called. 'Egyptians can do these things.'

'I think you over-estimate Egyptians.'

'You can say to people, don't come up the mountain and see god or the experience will kill you. The other possibility is, that if they went up the mountain, they would see nothing, no face, no voice. That Moses made the thing in his mind, and somehow – by poison, by the power of his eyes, forced us to see it too. I don't want to live with a man who does that sort of thing.'

'If you're a true rebel, you ought to go up the mountain. You ought to break the picture. You ought to show there is nothing there.'

'Or you ought to.'

'Me? I wouldn't dare.'

'You think Yahweh sits there and *has* a voice?'

'I suppose I do.'

'Amazing. A civilised man.' And he turned and went his way.

The Lawgiver's Absence, and human Sacrifice

When Moses had been on the mountain top about a month, the rumour went round that he'd died up there. That Joshua had taken the food to a proper place for collection and found yesterday's food there, uncollected by Moses, untouched.

I can remember getting very depressed by the rumour. There wasn't anyone else there who could get us out of the wasteland.

About that time some clansmen of clan Gideon let it be known that they hadn't been wasting their time in the Horeb area. That they had been brewing a palm wine in vats the whole month, and now it was just about ready.

The rumour that Moses was dead went hand in hand with the talk of a great big palm wine binge coming soon. The idea of Yahweh on the summit didn't hold much force in the camp any more. For example, one night I went walking and found myself near the tent of Naom. I saw groups of men and women sitting together, laughing, looking slack, as if they had already started on the palm wine. From nowhere, Joannah approached me. I heard her voice at my elbow.

'Love, they say he's dead. And if he's dead, the law's dead too.'

I felt her knuckles kneading my side. I felt a little annoyed that she had given me up so utterly and now instantly wanted me back.

'If he's dead, no one can lead us back to areas of plenty. Everyone is going to rot in the desert. Lovers too.'

'All the more reason, love,' she said, 'for lovers to taste each other now.'

Of course she was right about that. 'Come on,' I said. I turned in a direction that led out of the camp.

'Out among the rocks?' she asked, a little offended. Indeed she had soft flesh on her back, and the floor of the desert was too stony for her.

'I have a thick rug,' I said. 'Come with me, love.'

Without his brother's presence, Aaron behaved awkwardly. Some boys who stole jewellery from the treasure wagon got a sort of suspended judgment from him. He said to them, 'My brother will announce the right penalties when he comes back.'

The boys smirked at each other. It was easy for criminals to decide that the law-giver would not ever come down the mountain again.

I saw Aaron one day as he hustled down an alley of tents. He looked more like an unpopular schoolmaster than a tribal leader.

'They're saying he's dead,' I called to him.

'That's impossible.' As if he didn't want to talk about it.

'Do you believe he's dead?'

'No. It just wouldn't be right. A god doesn't bring you all this way, using human instruments, and then kill the instruments. You have to remember, these are his bride people.' And he gestured round him at the people. Fly-blown people, holes in their clothing. Lacking a wash, lacking good manners. Trapped leaderless in a little pocket of pasture. No longer digging latrines. Crapping close to the tents. Lacking pride. Waiting round for an orgy to creep up on them, once the palm wine was ready.

Aaron sighed. 'It isn't human. It satisfies someone like my brother, an educated man, to have a god to whom there's no image. It satisfies his brain. It doesn't satisfy ordinary people.'

'You've thought of something?'

'In Egypt, bull calfs are gods. The god's name is Apis. I once had a certain weakness for Apis. Even though my parents were fairly strict. Someone explained to me, some priest in Pithom, that the statue of the bull calf was not the god but the footstool on which the god stood. Yet people were aware of the god by seeing the statue.'

'You believe Yahweh needs a footstool here?'

Aaron screwed his face up. 'Perhaps Yahweh doesn't. But the tribe needs something it can see.'

I said, 'I'll watch what you do. With some interest.'

'It's easy for you,' he said.

What happened was this. A great part of the gold ornaments that were held in the treasure wagons were brought to a stone kiln set up on an edge of the camp. Also various tribeswomen came forward with little donations of golden trinkets. They seemed very excited and wore garlands of desert flowers. They were going to have a god they could see. They were going to have a centre to their camp. And all the good things that follow from having a centre, pride, order, a place to be enthusiastic, would follow. Two kiln men, stripped to the waist, stirred the golden mixture in the kiln. The frightening heat of melting gold beat against their faces and their flesh. Women stayed to watch and sing, and girls to dance.

> *'Where will our wedding, wedding be?*
> *Up in the fronds of a Dikla tree.*
> *What will we drink? What will we eat?*
> *The moon for wine and the sun for meat . . .'*

And the kilnsmen paddled away with their ladles as more gold went in. They had done the right thing, these men. They had lined the kiln with the right clays. When the gold was ready, a clay plug in the side of the kiln would be removed. The gold would run from the kiln into a stone trough. The trough would be bodily lifted and the gold poured into a sump of water near by. For Aaron, the magician, wanted to see how the gold would form itself once it was poured into water.

Aaron watched. His face was blank. I saw his sister Miriam come up to him.

'What shape will the creature be cast in?' she asked.

'I don't know. We'll have to see.'

'I can remember when you shamed our father Amram. By going to worship Apis, the calf god. I wouldn't mind betting. It'll be in the shape of a damn calf.'

'We'll have to see.'

'Your weakness brother,' she said, 'is that you see what you want to.'

'Leave me alone,' he said.

And indeed she was a hard woman. And he was just a tribesman, doing his best.

You could see the goldsmiths were really enjoying themselves, having a craft to perform again, no longer being mere nameless desert mice.

So the gold was melted and poured. Fifty or sixty men were needed to carry it in its stone troughs. When it was poured into water, Aaron bent over it. He read the shape the cooling gold took on as one reads the shape of clouds.

'There it is. It is – beyond doubt – the form of a bull calf.'

Though it was hard, on account of the crowd, to get in close, I got a glimpse of the indefinite shape of the gold as it went sharp and hard in the water. You could see horns, the sun resting on them. You could see a head section that *did* resemble a bull calf.

'We can make it,' said one of the goldsmiths. 'It won't even take long.'

So they began hammering out the gold into sheets. They worked behind a barricade of tenting, and only Aaron was allowed to look. Whenever he came out, he looked pretty satisfied.

'They are good. But you can tell that their hands are being helped by the god.'

When the statue was ready, tribesmen were let in behind the partition to build a mound of stones for it. Then, by means of rough pulleys, the type they had learnt to use as slaves in Egypt, they winched the calf into position.

The partitions were taken down, and in the lucid evening light, there stood the bull, the sun on its horns, its mouth set in a knowing line, knowing

'There it is. It is – beyond doubt – the form
of a bull calf'

The Lawgiver's Absence, and human Sacrifice

OVERLEAF 'The energy of those people that
night was amazing'

all-good and all-evil. Even to me it looked snide. It seemed to be saying, yes,
I'll look after you. I'll let you sing and bay and drink and rut. But I'm not yet
telling you the price I'll make you pay.

There was no doubt though, it was brilliantly constructed. The goldsmiths looked ecstatic. One of the wine-makers of the Gideon clan brought
forward a skin of palm wine and handed it to them. They drank a little and
then poured out some of it on the base of the stone mound where the bull-
calf stood.

Immediately this was done, all the home musicians there, harp players,
fluters, men with drums, women with tambourines, began singing and playing, and dancing began.

Aaron said to Miriam, 'I've saved them. Now they'll wait for my brother.'

'Tell me,' said Miriam. 'Is that thing really the footstool of Yahweh?'

'I have every hope . . .' said Aaron.

'Then that old lady had better watch herself.'

For an old woman, nearly blind, little able to climb, had somehow got up
the tumulus and was now caressing the golden beast. Then she turned to us,

on her face the same knowing grin as the bull-calf had. It made me shiver. And all the musicians stopped blowing, strumming, beating, to listen to what she said.

She said, 'You don't know what this god will ask of you.'

'This god?' Aaron asked. Confident again, he himself rushed to the base of the mound. 'This is not a god. This is the point where the god *Who Is* rests his foot. If we are fortunate.'

The old woman took no account of what he said. 'This is the sort of god,' she said, 'who comes up out of the bottom of the earth. A bull hopes to smell blood. We know it because, having smelt blood, a bull never forgets the smell.'

'That's untrue. That's her cracked old age talking.'

Aaron in fact was climbing the tumulus, finding it hard though, dragging at the old woman's ankles, willing to pull her off balance and break her back.

'There is the blood that flows from virgins,' the old woman said. 'There is the blood of living victims.'

'Animal sacrifice is enough,' Aaron kept raving. 'Elohim is not pleased to see people cut open.'

'Immediately this was done, all the home musicians there, harp players, flutes, men with drums, women with tambourines, began singing and playing, and dancing began'

The Lawgiver's Absence, and human Sacrifice

The old woman simply shrugged. As if Aaron was naïve. She tottered down the mound by herself. 'You'll all do what that calf wants. That's the way things turn out.'

She vanished then, probably to bed. What she had said worked on all the people who then began to sing and play and dance again.

It wasn't just that she had suggested this god might permit them to booze and womanise. It was as if she had said with the bull's voice, out of the same smile as the bull's, that the god would be pleased if they ran wild. And although Aaron made a speech denying it, the idea stayed planted in them.

Just the same, things stayed pretty quiet for the next week. Caleb, who was keeping order in the camp, punished a few drunks, warned a few fornicators. But he did not think that Joshua, on the mountain, need be disturbed.

One evening I saw Zipporah, Moses' desert wife, unpopular even with Miriam because of her strange background, standing near the flap of the leader's tent, listening to the noise from the tumulus where the calf stood.

'Will you go up and get him?' she called to me.

'No, I can't.'

'Will you take him by the shoulder and tell him he must come back?'

'I am very frightened of that mountain,' I admitted. 'You ought to ask someone like Dathan. They know there is no Yahweh up there.'

'This calf. I am very frightened. They might turn against foreigners. Me. You.'

'I can't go up.'

Though I would have been much safer if I had gone.

I stayed close to my tent. On the night of the trouble, I lay on my bed-roll listening to the hub-bub from the direction of the place where the calf stood. Without warning, it rose like a tide. What had happened was that someone, crazed with fervour, with visions induced by inhaling the right kind of grass, went into a coma, performed a coma dance. Strange voices came out of his mouth. The voices were not those of the man and they spoke in weird languages, harsh languages. Seeing this, part of the crowd became very excited. They beat up Caleb's young men. I believe that Aaron and Miriam both tried to speak but were beaten up and savaged. All I knew, quivering on my bed-roll, was that my tent flap was pushed back and at least two dozen men came in. They had torches. 'Where's the Cretan bastard?' they were yelling.

I noticed amongst them Naom, his features thick from the party, and Dathan, much clearer of eye, much sharper about the features.

They trussed me and carried me head-high through the camp. They half

ran, rushing me to the space around the calf. As we arrived, I heard some-one cheer. I was dumped close to the stone mound. The first thing I saw, propped up against the calf's front legs above me, was a girl with stark eyes. I noticed the eyes first, then the fact that she was naked. Finally the fact that she had been disembowelled. I couldn't believe it. Had she really been laid there as an offering?

Next I saw a stone table, perhaps half a dozen steps away. Five men stood around it. Four sang, an unrecognisable song. It was full of violent *uck* sounds. In their midst, leaning over a bowl that stood on the table, was the man in the coma. Now and then you saw the whites of his eyes. He seemed to stir the contents of the pot. Then he rolled his sleeves back and dipped his hand into the mouth of the thing. He drew out and showed to the crowd a sort of scarlet rope. It occurred to me what it was. The entrails of the girl who now sat horribly between the front hooves of the calf. The way some people look for visions among the entrails of chickens, he was looking for visions in human bowels.

As you can believe, I began whimpering. I was answered by a moan close to my left shoulder. I turned and saw a woman there, a middle-aged woman. I recognised her face. She'd been pointed out to me. They had found her alone by the well in Elim and had made her part of the tribe. She'd been given charge of a tent full of orphans. Often she went out of her way to say what good luck it had been to be picked up in Elim by the Israelis. She herself had been left to die there by her own tribe, because she had suffered some sort of

BELOW 'Many of the devotees of the calf were sleeping on the sand all around the mound'

continual bleeding and that was considered bad luck. But in Elim the bleeding had stopped. Now, in the name of the golden calf, and under the hand of the mad priest at the table, it was going to start again.

'Where is he?' she asked me. 'The good man?'

I couldn't answer her.

After the mad priest at the altar had again shown the girl's entrails, people began coupling in front of the altar. The two of us, writhing to get out of our ropes, must have looked like part of the general frenzy. It's a very disturbing thing, to see people coupling before your eyes when you are about to die. To hear their noises and smell their sweat. I wanted very much to be one of them. Mindless. Rutting away.

The energy of those people that night was amazing. You would have

thought one human sacrifice, one erotic stampede would have sufficed. Yet, at midnight, they took the foreign woman who lay near me and lifted her onto the table. Four of them held her, while the man in the coma made a long speech in a language I had not come across anywhere. All the time he made passes over her belly with his knife. When he put it in, her roar of protest quietened even that mob. But the mock priest went on busily butchering her. Gesturing all the time with the knife. Her blood splashed on me where I lay. With my buttocks and elbows, I made mad efforts to move away a little. But someone hit me on the head to encourage me to lie still.

The woman's red hot cry still carried down the valley below Horeb. Did Moses hear it on the mountaintop? Or did Caleb send for him? Or did Joshua get a message about what was happening down the valley? The legend says that Yahweh himself spoke to Moses, while Moses slept on the mountain summit with the stone tablets on which he had impressed in Aramaic writing the basic law of the tribe. But having heard, he picked up the tablets on which this basic law was imprinted and hurried downhill in the dark.

However he found out, all that matters is – he came.

In the small hours, while I lay very cold and sweating wildly, waiting my turn at the altar, Moses came back. With him was a small corps of Joshua's young men. They looked to be full of an authority that had been lacking in them the week before, the night before. They looked as if no one was going to beat them up this morning. When they marched in, many of the devotees of the calf were sleeping on the sand all around the mound. At least one of the mock priests had fallen asleep. The corpses of the young girl and of the middle-aged woman brought from Elim sat crookedly under the smiling calf. You could tell now, by the way, what his smile was about.

'It is broken,' Moses yelled. Some of the sleepers half heard him in their sleep. Few roused. 'It is broken,' he repeated. He roared again. His voice vibrated in an odd and horrible way.

Caleb began weeping and knelt in front of him. His young men had begun to call themselves Levites, a name taken from the name of Moses' clan.

'It wasn't the Levites,' he said. 'No Levite did any of this.'

'Why didn't the Levites stop it?'

'You weren't here. It happened to be beyond us.'

'Did you lose the wagons with the arms in them?'

'No. We still have the arms wagons.'

'All Levites should now go and arm themselves.'

Caleb and the others went off to obey him. Through the grey morning Aaron came staggering and fell in the dust to show how much he regretted it all.

'Someone's beaten you up?'

'Yes. It doesn't matter.'

'You are the priest of the people of Yahweh. No one has a right to beat you up. Even if the covenant is broken.'

Then he saw me. His eyes bulged. I wouldn't have thought he was so concerned for me.

'Zipporah?' he asked Aaron.

'She is safe. Miriam has hidden her away.'

He thought about this for a long time. When he spoke again it was with an icy measured anger, an Egyptian anger.

'My wife is not safe in my tribe? Is that how it's been?'

'Nobody has been safe,' said Aaron, beginning to sob. 'I have only a little grasp of what is happening . . .'

'But you gave them the calf?'

'Yes.'

'And then could not control it.'

'Yes.'

'And they beat their high priest?'

'High priest?'

'You, man. It is you I am talking about.'

'I don't feel like high-anything. But yes, they beat me.'

At that second, Moses seemed to remember me. He came across and cut me loose.

'I can't say,' he said, 'how ashamed I am. For them . . .'

'Can you stop it?' I was not yet convinced.

'I can stop it. Even my wife wasn't safe.'

Levites, fully armed, began arriving all round the edges of the place where the dancing had gone on for the past seven nights. When they had made more or less a military line, they marched forward. They lifted men by the hair and hacked at the sides of throats. I heard the gurgle of the dying. I could scarcely believe it.

'It's an extreme punishment,' I called out.

'One race has the true god,' he said 'We can't risk being cast off by him.'

'But all races think they have the true god. What if you merely think you have? Killing all these people. Not that they were friends of mine.'

'I am not deceived,' he said in his decreeing Egyptian manner. 'You know that. I am not deceived. I am the representative.'

And the Levites went on lifting men's heads and hacking the throats. And any women that they found there amongst the men, they woke them. And the women, of course, quickerly sobered and went away home.

'They will not forget,' said the law-giver in his awesome way.

I did not know it but one of the men now bleeding to death in front of their golden calf was Naom, husband of Joannah.

The law-giver marched round the camp. At his elbow, Joshua and Caleb blowing on rams' horns. They tugged at tent flaps, and slowly all the guilty people came out. As for me, I was taken to my tent and fell quickly but uneasily asleep. The record of the rest of the day I have from other people.

First Moses told all the tribal leaders that the covenant had been broken. He broke the stone tablets in front of their eyes. The punishment of the devotees of the golden calf went on all day. The five who had with their own hands held the sacrificial flesh of the young girl and the middle-aged strange-woman were tried. The calf was melted down again quickly in the kiln. The five were forced to kneel and a horn-cup of the molten metal was forced down their throats. I am glad I did not see them struggling and gasping as the smoke of their burning guts came out their mouths. It burnt its way right through them and passed out their anuses. So they tasted their god and died of it.

That punishment the Israelis never forgot. Small wonder!

I can see his reasons for punishing people the way he did. It was true: If he had not been strong then, the tribe would have been lost to Yahweh. But now punishments snaked through the tribe as that gold snaked through the bodies of the human sacrifices. And the punishment was on an Asian, not an Egyptian scale.

Yet what was even more surprising, most of the tribesmen accepted it. Joannah would always consider her husband's execution was unfortunate but not unjust. I was only beginning to see how deeply the old ideas moved in that tribe. That they were desert tribesmen and had brought their one god out of the desert. That although they were slaves in Egypt, they were really that one-god's one people. And that if they were wildly unfaithful to that one-god, no punishment was too bad for them.

Later, in drumming up support for his revolt, Dathan, who somehow escaped the reprisals, would talk about the brutal way the calf-worshippers had been treated. Yet it was not a living issue with the tribe. To the mind of the tribesman, the death of the calf-worshippers was a hard fact but one they could accept.

The behaviour of the calf-worshippers told Moses this: That the tribe needed somehow to see Yahweh; that there were a lot of craftsmen like the goldsmiths in the camp, who had had crafts which they were not exercising any more. Before he went back up the mountain to make out new tablets of the law, he ordered that weavers, carpenters, metal-workers be put to work in making a grand tent for Yahweh in the midst of the camp.

In this tent the tablets of the law would be kept. In it, too, a sealed pot of the manna by which the race was surviving. Yahweh would live there, in the tent, and in a wooden ark in which the tablets would be placed, Yahweh's heart would beat. And twice a day there would be sacrifices made there. Clean sacrifices. First-born animals. Offerings of bread and wine and oil.

Some people saw an interesting little exchange between Zipporah and Miriam.

Zipporah approached Miriam. 'I must thank you for saving me from those who might have sacrificed my body. I thank you all the more because you don't very much like me.'

'I would have saved anyone,' said Miriam, 'from *those* people.'

The Lawgiver puts up a Tent for Yahweh

One day, with great singing and drum beating, the tablets of the law were locked inside a decorated wooden casket called the Ark. And this itself put inside the tent which was Yahweh's dwelling-place. The tent itself was slung over acacia-wood pillars. The tent material was heavy and dyed red with scarlet dyes taken from cochineal insects. An acacia-wood altar having, like the Ark, long handles on either side of it, stood in front of the tent where Yahweh lived. And all round the tent and the altar stood a fence of woven and embroidered linen.

Of course it was rather crude at the start. But the practice of the priesthood who worked there, around Yahweh's Ark, grew more and more exact as the years passed. For example, there was a particular kind of incense that had to be burnt in the sanctuary, in front of the tent of the Ark. As a young man, Moses had learnt how to make Egyptian incense, and how the Assyrians and the Philistines who burnt children made their incense. The incense burnt in front of Yahweh was to be different.

The story goes about these days that Aaron's two sons, Nadab and Abiu, burnt the wrong sort of incense in front of Yahweh's tent. When they didn't come out after burning the incense, their father Aaron went in after them. He found them, so the legend goes, stretched dead on the sand in front of the altar of incense. Yahweh had struck them dead for burning foreign incense in front of his tent.

Now, this story *is* just a legend, told these days to make priests careful. Do your job properly, or like Nadab and Abiu, your brain will burst! That sort of thing.

The two unfortunate young men in fact died of contagious fever that ran through the Israeli camp. But since the two of them died at the one time, even there under Horeb it was presumed that they must have done things wrongly in front of the tent of Yahweh.

To return to the day that the tablets were put in the Ark, the Ark in the tent, when Moses set up a holy place for the Israelis in the midst of their camp. He presented Aaron and Aaron's sons to the entire tribe. These men, he said, would sacrifice the young bullock as a burnt offering, the two rams, the basket of unfermented bread. He then clothed Aaron in vestments that

had been specially made. A blue tunic that had bells on it, to ensure Aaron would never enter Yahweh's tent unannounced.

When the robing was over, Moses went around the tent enclosure of the Ark and poured oil over all its tables and implements. It was oil that had survived in a stone phial in Moses' pocket while Moses was in the presence of Yahweh. Then the residue of the oil was poured over the forehead of Aaron.

Next the young bullock was slaughtered by Moses himself. Aaron and his sons laid their hands on its head, to show it was done with their consent. With the blood of the young bullock, Moses smeared the acacia-wood altar inside the enclosure. The rest of the blood was poured away into the sand. Various sprinklings of blood followed as the rams too were sacrificed. The idea was that all the tribesmen were guilty and should die, but that Yahweh

'A blue tunic that had bells on it, to ensure
Aaron would never enter Yahweh's tent
unannounced'

BELOW 'The tablets of the law were locked inside
a decorated wooden casket called the Ark'

would accept the substitute sacrifices. Therefore Moses smeared Aaron's
right ear, his right thumb, and the great toe on his right foot. The dominant
side of Aaron's body was by these means rendered clean. At one stage the
tribe itself, outside the tent and the enclosure, was sprinkled with blood. So
that they would be safe staying there, so close to Yahweh.

If you don't think it sounds impressive, you should have been there. It
was spell-binding. And to see Aaron, the man who had made the mistake of
the golden calf, transformed, standing in the entrance to Yahweh's tent with
twelve precious stones, filched from the Egyptians, on his chest. One stone
for each clan.

From that day the complicated law of the tribe came into stronger and

'In this hollow middle, are clans called the Gersonites
and the Merarites carrying Yahweh's tent
and the Ark of the Covenant with Yahweh'

OVERLEAF 'And above the dust of their travel,
they carried standards, great wooden plaques,
just like Egyptian divisions'

stronger use. The washings connected with eating and sex, the prohibitions concerning eating and sex, the wise rules against touching flesh-eating animals, pigs who carry diseases on four fat legs, preying birds, shell-fish. The complications of sabbath keeping. For it is complicated, the extreme way they keep the sabbath. I saw in my day ordinary Israeli soldiers axed down where they stood rather than take up heavy weapons on the sabbath. Who am I to say it's all a bit excessive?

And in all the tribe's long history, they never again laid prostitutes in front of Yahweh's tent, sodomised each other close to the sanctuary, or spilt human blood there. You have to admire them. What other races can make such boasts about their sanctuary.

After a census was taken in Horeb, the tribe moved on. One of Zipporah's brothers was guide.

All the clans had an order of march now. They moved in the manner of an Egyptian army. The same way Rameses had organised his army when marching towards Syria, Moses now organised his tribe. First came Judah, Gideon, Levi, in a solid line. Then two columns with a hollow middle. In this hollow middle, are clans called the Gersonites and the Merarites carrying Yahweh's tent and the Ark of the Covenant with Yahweh. Then a solid line again made up of the Ruben, Symian, Gad clans. And again two hollow lines in the midst of which another clan called the Kohathites carried all the furnishings of the sanctuary itself, the outer partitions, the various tables. At the end marched again a solid block made up of Dan, Asher and Napthali. So the tribe was a substantial rectangle now, with two sacred hollows in it. If you withdrew from it and looked at it from a distance, you could understand why – from now on – only the largest tribes would ever attack it. And above the dust of their travel, they carried standards, great wooden plaques, just like Egyptian divisions. You could see the lion painted on the standard of Judah, the human which represented Ruben's clan, the ox for Ephraim, and the eagle for Dan.

They moved on some days from Horeb. Where they camped then, a great flock of quails again came in, were again captured and dried in the sun. While the good eating was still going on, a plague broke out in the camp. People went into a fever. The points of their cheeks and the hollows under their eyes went blue. Often they bled from the nose or the mouth, the ears or the back passage. One of Joannah's stepchildren, a son of Naom by her earlier marriage, died this way, and as I have already mentioned, two of Aaron's sons. There was a lot of talk about how the deaths were due to people gorging themselves with bird meat. I myself think there was something wrong with the wells in that place.

I generally travelled with the Levi tribe. So I was always within shouting distance of Moses' tent. One day, it was Miriam I heard roaring at Moses' tent flap. In a way I am an idle fellow – I like watching arguments. I went out to watch this one.

'Before the virtue goes out of you,' Miriam was saying. 'You can't expect Yahweh to tolerate it. Sharing a bed with a low breed, an Arab. It's a wonder he hasn't forbidden it to you.'

'She is not an Arab,' Moses told her.

'You're the law-giver. You're empowered to put her aside.'

'Don't talk to about that.'

'If you don't, the strength will pass out of you. The Voice will stop speaking. Let her go back to her people.'

'They are not Arabs,' Moses said again. That accusation had somehow stung him.

Aaron was there too, more composed than his sister. 'She's right,' he said.

'They are a seemly people,' said Moses. 'Their rituals are decent. They are our cousins. They are not Arabs. No more than us.'

'She looks like an Arab,' Miriam hissed. 'She has that low-grade look.'

'I think you're beyond yourself,' said Moses, raising his voice a little. 'It's beyond debating. Come with me right away.'

He walked off quickly in the direction of the sanctuary, where Yahweh's tent was pitched. Ordinary people, even women, could bring the beasts they were offering inside the tenting partitions that surrounded the sanctuary. They could not however touch the various altars or go near the tent that stood there.

Moses led his brother and sister in through the partitions. Curious people like myself crowded round the entrance, not daring to go in just for the sake of watching a family brawl.

'You two lie on that side of the sanctuary,' said the Representative, 'I on this side. If loving a Midian wife is foul in Yahweh's eyes, you will see the signs in my body. You will see the strength vanish.'

We watched them prostrate themselves. Aaron sensibly using a mat to save the priestly clothes which were precious to the whole tribe. But Miriam, being a headlong woman, threw herself wildly down on the dusty sanctuary.

Nothing happened for a long time. Some of the spectators shrugged and walked away. Then I heard a rattle in Miriam's throat. It grew to be a long moan, a protest. She sat up looking at her hands and moaning. And as she looked at her hands, all the curious in the doorway saw her face. It was all soft, white, rotten with leprosy. There was a great leper's lump on the side of her neck. A terrible sore in the corner of her mouth.

I found myself reeling away from the sanctuary, wanting to find Joannah and tell her. I was groaning as I went, really shocked. I didn't doubt that I had seen what I'd seen, that Miriam's flesh had gone instantly leprous.

That wasn't the only time I saw her in this terrible state. That afternoon, she came back to her tent, which was near mine. She called to her daughters, Rachel and Leah. They came out and wailed. She wailed in return. Yet she didn't protest about being covered with soggy white flesh and ulcers.

'This is what I have earned, daughters, for speaking badly to the man Yahweh chose. Learn, learn. Bring out my bed-roll and my goat's hair cloak. Bring out a skin of water and a little food. Put it in the sand. Do not touch me. I must live separate from you now, separate from the tribe.'

And with much wailing, all this was done and the pitiful woman limped away. I remember thinking even at the time, it's a lot of punishment for a sharp-tongued bitch. I have known sharp-tongued bitches that get away with terrible evil very easily.

Sometimes we met people, small friendly groups, *bedu*. Small trading caravans. One day, a splendid-looking Ethiopian scout on a fine camel. Aaron and Moses spoke to him. It wasn't a very successful interview I believe.

Later I saw him sitting by himself, near a fire, eating a piece of sheep shank. Wrapped in his cloak, sitting upright, his own man. I could just see the black corner of his face. On impulse I took him some wine. He swigged.

'You seem a sensible man,' he said. He said it as if he hadn't met many sensible men lately.

'Why do you say so?'

'You're not like them. You don't make big claims.'

'You met Prince Moses?'

'Prince?'

'He used to be a prince in Egypt.'

'He still can't get into Canaan from here. That's what he wants. He wants me to act as guide from here to Canaan. Not an impossible journey in itself. But what happens when the king of Edom or the cities north of Kadesh hear that we are coming? They're tough people, with paid armies. Paid armies. We'll be met, don't you worry, before we get anywhere near Canaan. We'll find paid soldiers formed up either side of our road. Throwing things at us. Sharp things. Tough bastards.'

'So you refused to work for us.'

'I take on reasonable jobs.'

'We can manage the king of Edom,' I boasted, as if I'd been born in the tribes of Israel. I don't know what got into me.

'Your god has promised you Canaan, I believe?' he said sarcastically. Then he dropped his voice. 'If, of course, there were any reasonable people, who wanted to pay me to guide them in a reasonable direction, back to Egypt say, I would be very interested in a job like that.'

I thought of Dathan. This man would be a godsend to Dathan.

'I can't think of anyone,' I told the Ethiopian.

It was just after he rode away, looking elsewhere for work, that Miriam came dancing into the camp, singing in her best voice. She was clean of all traces of leprosy. She was singing how people should congratulate her, because out amongst the stunted acacias she had gone to sleep a leper and woken up a clean woman, an acceptable woman without sores. She sang to Yahweh for his mercy and said how clever she thought Yahweh had been with this week long leprosy. She would not bad-mouth her brother again, she said.

You couldn't watch her now without smiling. People kissed her regardless of infection. For there was nothing to catch now.

When I saw her face all unblemished, I thought, yes I said the right thing in telling the Ethiopian scout to go his way. Who would ever want to leave the tribe in which things like this happened?

Even so, they put me through a long wait before I could marry Joannah, and even then I was a second-class tribesman. They would not circumcise me until I had passed examinations in the law of the tribe. I must admit, I was willing to postpone *that* privilege.

The oasis of Kadesh to the north was our next aim. But on the way we made a number of desert camps. During these camps, I would often sit in the shade by Moses' tent flap. The idea was that I would see the law administered and learn something of it. Besides that, you picked up all the gossip sitting there, and were first with the latest news.

It was the morning after a desert Sabbath. Now the leader was still very strict about Sabbath rest. He really believed that if the people were ever to have the vision, they must sit at least one day, quiet in the shade, waiting for . . . messages? He believed, too, that it was only a proper compliment to Yahweh. The idea was that on the seventh day you did nothing in the matter of water and food, showing that you knew your desert god would provide them afresh in the morning.

However, on this particular morning, a tribal leader came to Moses' tent. The Levites or police or whatever you want to call them had brought to him, the day before, four men who had been gathering palm fronds during the Sabbath. The tribal leader had warned them, but in the afternoon they had all been caught again, picking up acacia sticks for the evening fire.

'That's it.' the leader said to Moses. 'They just don't consider light work is wrong. So I go on imposing little fines on them. But it does no good.'

'It does no good,' said Moses, a little harshly, 'because you let them see that you think they are reasonable and I am not.'

'Perhaps. Is it any use? All this sweat over a little bit of kindling?'

Moses said, 'It is owed. It is owed, and we will give it to him. The day without blemish. Listen, you think it's nothing to pick up a bit of kindling on the day. What I say is, it would be better to go out and build a statue, slaving hard all day. A work with a bit of grandeur. Not a mean little act like gathering twigs. As if there'll be no twigs tomorrow . . .'

'You're right, of course,' said the tribal leader. In fact you could see Prince Moses' arguments biting into him a bit. 'But from the point of the view of the average man, they are right too.'

'I didn't bring them this far to make them average men.'

'Anyhow, I don't know what more to do with them. A little fine? But next Sabbath they'll be at it again.'

'What have you in mind?'

'There is this – a law broken by ordinary tribesmen, over and over, is a law that will probably never be properly kept. And a law that ordinary people can never properly keep is probably . . .'

'A bad law, do you say? *A bad law?*'

'What do I do with them? That's what I want to know.'

'The whole tribe will find out how to keep the day. They'll have no doubt after this. We'll stone the offenders to death.'

The tribal leader said nothing. In a sort of daze, he even half turned away from the leader.

'The Levites will do it,' Moses went on. 'No men of cruel nature will pick up a stone, only the Levites.'

'It is a terrible death,' muttered the tribal leader.

'I don't deny it's sad for them.'

Sitting under a tent flap, I thought, *that's big-minded of you.*

'They'll be taken out of the camp and tied to stakes. Before the stones are thrown, Joshua will explain what is to happen and why. There will, of course, be a crowd.'

'Perhaps an angry crowd.'

'The whole tribe will understand. I'm not just thinking of the tribe we have here now, in the Paran desert. I'm thinking of the nation not yet born. They will always know, from the story of these two men, how to keep Sabbath.'

The tribal leader was still pale. His voice dim. 'No one believes in the tribe's future more than I do. But I do not want to see what you do to the men in question.'

'Of course you must see it. They are of your clan.'

'Do you want to tell them to their face?'

'I have no reason to see them.'

'I will have the executions carried out before the next Sabbath.'

'It will be done before sunset.'

The tribal leader nodded, swallowed, staggered out.

After the worst of the day's heat was over, most of the tribe, except Moses himself, walked a little to the west of the camp. Here, under a low cliff totally innocent of any green growth, four poles had been dug into the earth. The men were roped to the poles, their arms above their heads. From all the scree at the base of the cliffs, the Levites had made a long pile of stones about twenty paces from the men. Four young Levites, chosen men, stood on this pile. From it they would choose stones to hurl, one after another, at the four men.

The young victims called out across the pile of stones and the four set-faced executioners to the crowd beyond. Did they have relatives there? Or had kind neighbours kept their parents and young wives at home? 'People,

OVERLEAF 'It is a slow death. The prisoners weave about on their poles'

we have done nothing. It's your turn next week. Turn over in bed next Sabbath and this is where you'll end.'

Standing amongst the crowd, I saw everyone around me was strangely passive. Awed perhaps. You could tell there was not going to be a mob rush to save the victims. The four victims *thought* there would be. And the crowd's knowledge that there would *not* be embarrassed the crowd. They could not not look at the condemned men full on. Even the people who thought like Dathan were merely sullen. They were willing to let these deaths happen. They knew that later these deaths could be used as a good argument against Moses' way.

So it was painful to hear one of the victims call, 'Tell my wife not to go running off with anyone yet. I'll be home this evening.' Till the first stone landed on him, and maybe even later, he thought the exercise would be called off before real harm was done.

The tribal leader, then Joshua, mounted a boulder and spoke of the importance of this day. That the way speech separated man from the animals, *the day* separated Israelis from slaves and other races. And then Joshua told the young executioners to begin.

It is a slow death. The prisoners weave about on their poles and are even able to duck some of the stones. It takes a long time for the skin to break open on the forehead or face or chest. When the blood is evident, women in the crowd begin to wail. But by the end, there are even some people laughing, the shock of it. At last the ribs are broken and who knows what else. The victim opens his mouth piteously and teeth and blood fall out. The four exhausted Levites are replaced by four others. Their faces are mute. They aim for the head and the heart.

How long is it before they die? Half an hour or an hour or two hours. The stone throwers don't stop when apparent death has taken place. For they have no blood lust. They are neither satisfied or unsatisfied, they are acting for the leader and – could it be? – for Yahweh. Before they are finished throwing, the crowd goes home.

As far as we knew, Moses had never carried a weapon while living amongst the Hapiru, or been specially guarded by Joshua's young men. But Joshua wisely insisted on placing armed Levites round the leader's tent. An angry crowd came, right enough. Seeing the armed men, they did not try to force their way into Moses' tent, but Dathan and others made speeches. They were good speeches.

'We were all forced to come with him right enough. Because he went to the trouble to make our names stink with the Egyptians. And so we came, losing people here and there of fevers, living a barbarous life of the type we

were not used to, eating poor food to conserve our flocks for the day that we entered our kingdom in the north. If we complained, not having wanted to come in the first place, we were ungrateful. We were being brought to Horeb though, and on Horeb we would receive a law that would make it all worthwhile. We have been to Horeb. And the law we received was that for gathering sticks on a particular day of the week, we deserve a long, slow death. The nonsense of the Sabbath law is a worse slave-master than Merneptah or Rameses ever were. The gift of the law is a stone hurled at our heads. The fruit of the law is murder.'

At the end of one such speech, Moses appeared at his tent door. The noise from the crowd was immense. Moses argued with Joshua to be let through the cordon of armed men. By insisting, he was at last allowed to come out and speak to the crowd.

He could not be heard though for catcalls and boos. The leaders of the opposition had to walk around, quietening people. They were sure that, by speaking, Prince Moses would only weaken his position.

'Do you believe that I am a murderer? Or do you believe that Yahweh is a murderer as well? If you believe either, come and take me. I deserve to be destroyed. Come on, Dathan. If I am evil and Yahweh is evil, then I have no protection. Not even against you, a man who helped organise the sacrifice of humans and, by accident, escaped punishment for it.'

But no one was willing to touch him. Though Dathan made another good speech out of it. 'You speak like that because the Levites are not yet sick of you. Nor are all of the tribes. We intend to allow you time. Enough to destroy yourself.'

'You call today murder,' Moses said. 'You call the law murder. A man who calls the law murder does not have enough time left either to make a gift of it to himself or to me. Remember that, Dathan.'

'The leader threatens me,' Dathan yelled exultantly. 'Do you hear it? The leader threatens me.'

'I do not threaten vengeance. I announce it. I have no right to the silly emotion of vengeance. I do not feel it now. I did not feel it today. But remember it and be warned, Dathan. I announce vengeance.'

The crowd started to go home then. Moses called after them, 'Tribesmen, don't be deceived. The law is life, not death. You will see. Today was like the death of chaff so that the grain might make flour.'

Though I and many others around were impressed by what he'd said, we were still uncertain. Had today's stoning been an act of life, or an act of death? If you asked the two poor bastards that had been stoned, I know what they would have said.

One morning soon after, very early, I saw Moses come out of his tent and stagger across the stony floor of the Wilderness of Paran, as though in some sort of trance.

'Ahiiiii!' he screamed. 'What if I give up now? What if I become a tribesman? Like any other ordinary man? What if you made Joshua in my place? Or Caleb? Maybe I am willing anyhow to disobey you. You can only strike me down, as you have struck down others. Maybe I'm not afraid of going to my peace in the earth.'

After a while he turned round and found me there.

'He will not let me go,' he told me. He began sobbing. 'He will not let me *go.*'

'Do you want to be let go, my lord?'

'Who could doubt it? And they throw dung at my wife and call her an Arab. And they throw small stones at my sons, and say soon it will be big stones.'

'Won't you be rewarded? By Yahweh?'

'Never. Never that I know of. Never that he has said. Never that he has given me a glimpse of.'

'He promises you nothing?'

'Only that he will ride me the way a horseman rides his horse. And that there will be a nation. And a promised land. And that the tribesmen will be the nation. And that the land will be called by their name. Israel.'

Barely reported, Moses' words could have seemed merely the self-pity of a chieftain who has tried to be harsher than he ought to be and seen his tribe turn against him. But in fact there was such real agony in the man, and such grand faith in the truth of what he was doing, that I immediately found myself on my knees, hugging his knees.

I said, 'Lord, not all your tribe hates you or your wife or your sons.'

But Moses just looked out across the wilderness. 'Could you take a message to Joshua,' he said. 'Tell him to blow the trumpets. We'll all be happier when we get to Kadesh.'

The Lawgiver sends out Spies

But before we reached the pastures of Kadesh, Moses sent out a spy from each tribe to travel north and investigate the land of Canaan, promised to the tribe by Yahweh. All the tribe came in front of the tent of Yahweh, and Moses announced the twelve. Shammua, son of Zaccur of the Reuben clan. Shaphat, son of Hori of the Simeon clan. Caleb, son of Jephunneh, of the tribe of Judah. And so on. Igal, Joshua, Palti, Gaddiel, and other strong-minded young men.

From his brothers-in-law and various desert scouts he had met, Moses had a large hearsay knowledge of the land to the north. He lost no chance of telling the tribe that it would be their land, and in schooling them in its geographic details. On the day the twelve spies were sent out, he made this speech.

'First you will cross a desert to our north. You are used to desert now. Brown, flat-topped hills. Suddenly you will come amongst wooded mountains, through ravines where you must be very careful. By following the normal trade routes though, you should come to no harm. First you will find Beersheba, and to the north the fine city of Hebron. Continuing on north you will come into a deep valley where the grapes will be in season at this time of year. And beyond it you will find the plain on which all the goods of the earth grow, and cattle graze on good grass. But the people you see there – remember that Yahweh has taken away their right to that land and given it to you. Bring back whatever fruits are in season so that all of us can see them. Find out such things as, how many cities does Hebron control? Do they have walls or are they open towns? Do the kings of the area keep regular armies? If so, how are these armies equipped? Do they look like good soldiers or poor? Of one thing you can be sure. They are a people lost and uncircumcised. Their rites are foul. They worship idols of stone. Walk in stealth, but know in your hearts that you are the kings of that land. And behave, accordingly, with courage.'

After they had all gone, the tribe moved on to Kadesh. It was a broad grassland separating one desert from another. A number of springs came out of its hills and fed it. It was such a good place that the tribe would be too willing to stay on here.

Meanwhile, the spies were travelling through a great sandstone ravine and coming into superb watered country, rich in pomegranates, figs, grape vines. They were picking the new fruit from the trees.

It was six weeks before they came back. They had spied out not only fruit but cities and armies. In front of the tabernacle, they made their report to Moses and the people. It would have been better if he had interviewed them separately, privately. He did not know that ten of the twelve scouts were about to deny him support.

Joshua spoke first. 'The city of Hebron is a fair city. It was built six years before Tanis in Egypt. Its walls are a thousand paces by four hundred. It stands on a mountain and it has deep wells. From Hebron a Hittite king controls twenty sizeable towns. His army is Philistine. It includes some of the giant tribe of Anak. This is a fair city where we can begin. Once we have a city of our own, we are less assailable. If they have heard of us at all in Hebron, they think we are desert raiders. They would not consider that we want their city in which to settle. The surprise of our desires will defeat them.'

This speech was clapped, well enough. Then Shammua got up to speak for the group he had led.

'I am very pleased my brother Joshua takes such a happy view of the land he has entered. I myself travelled into the hill country of the Jebusites. It is full of walled cities – a walled city on a hill every five miles. I want to know, how does a desert tribe break into a walled city? How does a tribe with no proper army deal with a paid army? For they have Philistines and a core of the giant Anaks, too.'

Next Shaphat. 'We happened to see a regiment of their army bathing in a river. This was in the valley of Elah, amongst the mountains. They are large men. They have round leather hats to protect them in battle. Even their laughter makes one hesitate. I would like to think the land was ours. It looked, however, like theirs.'

The spy Igal: 'I visited the mountains of the Amorites and came down east towards the great Salt Sea, which they call the Dead Sea. The situation that Shammua describes prevails here. There are many fortifications. Admittedly, open towns. But if we took an open town, we would in turn have it taken from us. Down by the Salt Sea are the Canaanites. A cultivated people. They don't walk as if they know their rites are foul. They have no doubts in themselves. Their army again is made up of their own people, of mountain people, and the giants of Anak.

Shaphat: 'We haven't the numbers. We haven't the weapons.'

Caleb, who had travelled with Joshua, became angry. 'This is nonsense. We can take Hebron now. We should take Hebron now, before the whole world knows of our ambitions. They are strong, yes. But we have Yahweh. He will live in our camp. Who lives in their city? The walls will crumble in front of us.'

But there was an outcry from the other scouts. And you could tell that *these* were the ones who counted with the crowd. Weren't they fine young men, those ten who contradicted Caleb and Joshua? Weren't they Levites, willing to stone criminals to death? Hadn't they been brave against the tribe of Amalek?

Without saying anything more, Moses walked back to his tent. I caught up with him.

'You must be disappointed?' I said.

'They are brave and reasonable young men,' he said, smiling faintly in his Egyptian way. 'They have learnt to think in terms of fitting the means to the task. It is what they learnt from my grandfather Rameses. But yes, I am dis-appointed. As a man is in a wife who is always maligning him or taking strangers into her body.'

That night there was a riot in the camp. Stones were thrown. Moses was knocked down, and Joshua. That night, too, a plague was felt in the camp of the Israeli Hapiru. It was the plague we had seen before. Fever, bluish ulcers on the flesh after a day or so. It appeared first amongst the scouts. One could only believe that they had caught it in the land of Canaan. Igal died of it. Shaphat, Shammua, and nearly all the others. Joshua and Caleb showed no symptoms.

Joannah and I stayed in our tent, avoiding contact with anyone. Since we were newly married, it wasn't an unpleasant restriction on our movements. Except that she looked wide-eyed, expecting all the time to develop the fever herself.

She said, 'This is a judgment on the tribe. Master Moses wanted them to go into Canaan. And they wouldn't go. This is the judgment.'

'Can you be sure?'

'There's nothing that just happens in this tribe. It all has a meaning. It is easy to understand what the meaning is. Yahweh sent the Egyptians plagues because they angered him. And now us, we have a plague for the same reason.'

I put my hand to her cheek and said, 'I don't think Yahweh wants your sweet flesh, my dove.'

'Don't say it.'

She was a true tribeswoman. Once a plague started, they all thought Yahweh was there, in their tents. Not just *there* in a poetic sense, but *there* as a member of the family, a great being who made great demands yet somehow promised great freedoms.

'I want to go into Canaan,' I confessed to her as I had to Moses. 'I want to return to the world.'

'This is your world,' she said, a little hurt.

'I wasn't born in a desert, and neither were you.'

During this plague, a young Levite came to our tent. He stood outside, begging to be let in.

'How do I know you have not been with the dead?' my wife yelled at him.

'All right,' he said, 'I'll talk to him through the tent wall.'

This seemed reasonable. We had a low conversation, through the faded goat's hair of the tent which had once been Naom's.

'I believe,' he began, 'that you would like to die in a city.'

'Who told you that?'

'There are men in this camp who make sure everything the leader says is overheard.'

'Next morning two hundred families
moved north from Kadesh into the
Wilderness of Zin'

'What of it?'

'I am a member of a group who wish to move on into Canaan. We have
Yahweh's promise that it will be given to us.'

'What does the leader say?'

'The rumour is that he is very sick. He was, you might have heard, hit with
a stone. There is a further rumour that he has the plague.'

'I find that hard to believe.'

'In Canaan there is pleasant mountain country where even a small tribe
could live safely. If we increase our strength by fighting small armies, taking
small towns, in the end we will take a large one.'

'It is possible.'

'Will you come?'

'Speak to me again when the plague is over. Mention the names of important men in the tribe who also hope to go. I am, you can say, interested. If
Moses consents to the journey, even more interested still.'

He made a regretful noise beyond the woven wall. 'The leader will not be
going. He has gone back on what he earlier said. It seems now that Yahweh
no longer intends us to have Canaan. I find it hard to believe that the god
would change his mind just because a few people argued the point.'

'What is your name?'

'Abiram.'

'Then I will be visited by you again, Abiram?'

'Certainly.'

He did not leave immediately. I said, 'It's sad isn't it. Some wanting to stay
here in Kadesh, others wanting to go back to Egypt, others north towards
Hebron. A little disappointing.'

'Perhaps he brought it on himself.'

'Do you think so?'

'I'll call again when plans are more definite.'

The plague passed off. Joannah and I began to walk around the camp again.
One day we were stopped by a dark, young man.

'I am Abiram, who spoke to you through the tent wall.'

'Of what?'

'You know of what. Of going forward into Canaan.'

'And what is happening in that connection?'

'Tomorrow morning we will all begin to pack. Half the Levites are coming.
Koreh, one of Joshua's best men, is one of the leaders. Dathan another.'

'Dathan?'

'We need a popular man. Someone who can speak to people in ways they understand.'

'Half the Levites are coming. Will the other half try to stop you?'

'No. Joshua warns us against it. But he will not block our path.'

'What is his warning?'

'That Yahweh, who forced us out across the desert in the direction of Canaan, now wants us to loiter here. It is the very opposite of what he said on first returning. Moses says Yahweh has changed his mind, and Joshua chooses to believe him. I don't.'

Beside me, Joannah shuffled her feet in the dust.

'Will you come?' Abiram asked.

'There are dangers. In the ravines.'

'No one denies it.'

I looked at the red hills around the valley of Kadesh. No, I thought. I can't wait here half a lifetime. Next, I looked at Joannah.

'We'll come with you.'

'Don't let anyone stop you bringing your arms or your full flock.'

Next morning, two hundred families moved north from Kadesh into the Wilderness of Zin. Moses stood at the north end of the camp, saying quietly to each family as it passed, 'Don't march to the attack. Yahweh will not take your part. Amalekites and Canaanites will come at you, full force.'

On each family this quiet threat worked strongly. Some men called their families out of the column and decided not to go further. Everyone was quiet. It wasn't a very jaunty departure. We crossed a number of the dead rivers that traverse Zin. It was as bad a journey as any that had been made. A lot of the desert here is just gravel and sand dunes and sour grass. Even though it was early autumn, the daytime sun was ferocious. We avoided the town of Beersheba, passing it some miles to the east. That was because Koreh suspected the city kingdoms kept informers in frontier towns like that, their task to tell of large movements of tribesmen.

Beyond Beersheba we went into a pass through the hills. With delightful suddenness we came to a wide spring flowing out of the base of the hill. Wild fowl rode on its water. You could see fish nuzzling the stones on the bed of the spring. On the shore, all the trees and fruits that Joshua had promised. Dates. Pomegranates growing wild.

'Then I noticed, quite close on either side of
the track, tall soldiers in brown helmets and
black tunics appeared'

The Lawgiver sends out Spies

Joannah, who had vomited all the way across Zin, began recovering.

When we moved on, all the men except those with sick wives marched at
the front and the rear and either side of the column, carrying what arms they
had.

'Two-days' easy march,' Koreh promised. 'And then we come to a hill
town south of Hebron. All its people are forfeit. Their clothes, their weapons,
their money, all goes to our strength.'

But as we were marching through a pleasant though rather dark valley, I
saw a glint like rain on the side of the hill. Arrows fell on the front and rear of
the column, where most of the armed men were. Near me I saw a tribesman
with an arrow in his throat. He seemed quite calmly to shake his head,
trying to shake the missile out. Then his soul's blood burst out over his lips.
I felt sick from terror. I called out useless warnings to Joannah. She could not
hear me. She was somewhere in the centre of the column.

Then I noticed, quite close on either side of the track, tall soldiers in brown helmets and black tunics appeared. They were in proper ranks. Some terrible battle rant was played on their trumpets and they marched down the slope with their spears raised above their heads. They began fighting with Koreh's men at the front, so that the whole tribe was pushed backwards through the pass.

I record gratefully that the Israelis at the rear of the column also killed many of these Philistine professionals. Our way out of the pass therefore lay over a number of black-tunicked corpses.

As I marched crabwise in a southerly direction, I saw Joannah near by, also carried along in a ruck of her kinswomen. They were all wailing, and I did not blame them. 'Joannah,' I called, but she did not hear me.

Then I noticed, right at my side, Abiram bravely parry a Philistine infantryman and lay the man's guts out with a lance. Expecting that the enemy must be everywhere amongst us, I began to raise the weapon I carried. It was a pitiful thing, halfway between a hoe and an axe. Abiram saw me.

'Keep out of the way of the enemy,' he called.

He probably wisely thought that I would be needed to find water in the desert for any survivors of this rout. I should have also been exempt under tribal law, which says that the feeble hearted and those given to vomiting are not expected to bear arms.

For two days that little frontier army from Canaan followed us. At dawn, dusk and the middle of the night they came out of the hills and harried our flanks. They wanted to convince us never to come back. They killed a lot of men and even took off a small number of women and young children. They did what they liked with the flocks, killing them or driving them off. The brave young men who fought to protect us have had no honour in the history of the tribe. They are looked on as defectors, and the fact that many of them were killed or badly maimed is said to be the proper fruit of their disloyalty to the leader and to Yahweh. Well, at least I am grateful to them, and Joannah, and every one of us who straggled up to the well at Horma two days after the first attack. At Horma we were left alone. The Canaanite infantry vanished homewards.

When everyone had rested, Koreh and Abiram and Dathan strolled round the encampment, debating aloud what they would do. Anyone who wanted to could follow the debate by walking at their heels or waiting till they passed his tent.

'If we had had,' Abiram would say, 'all the Levites with us, and the leadership of Joshua, the Canaanites could not have driven us back into the wilderness. And we did not have Joshua with us because of his loyalty to one man, Moses. Moses says Yahweh has told him that none of our generation will enter Canaan.'

'But how do we know, how does Joshua know, that Moses does not tell us this simply to divide and confuse the tribe?' Dathan would say.

A tribesman, with a wound in the head, might perhaps call out, 'I did not see you in the fighting, Dathan.'

For Dathan was fully as craven as I am.

The debate would continue.

'Will we ever move into Canaan?' Koreh would ask.

'Of course,' Dathan would say passionately. 'Having seen it, who could not return? But with the full tribe. Even with Moses if he wishes to come.'

'But with Moses as leader?' Abiram would ask.

'It is impossible. Who could respect him as a leader?'

Nearly everyone in the encampment had lost a husband or wife or child. Yet this daring public debate helped them to believe that their loss was the fault of Prince Moses.

So they looked forward to their return to Kadesh. They saw Moses, not the regular soldiers of Canaan, as their enemy.

Meanwhile Joannah and I kept quiet. I had come to my own conclusions. The cities of Canaan would not easily let us take their wooded highlands and rich valleys from them. I would be happy in Kadesh for the next two or three years and not hanker after any more expeditions northwards.

Yet the leaders went on debating. 'What we need, for victory,' said Koreh, 'is the tabernacle of the god *Who Is* in the midst of our encampment.'

The Lawgiver puts the Onus on Yahweh

One mid-morning we arrived back at Kadesh and simply pitched our tents amongst all the others that were already there. But Koreh, Dathan and Abiram, together with a man of the clan Ruben, still went throughout the entire camp, debating aloud. Even the Levites, those almost professional policemen and soldiers, who – because of their office – were considered members of Moses' clan, were divided in two.

The next morning I went humbly to Moses' tent and sat like a student of the law in the shade of his tent flap. I could hear he and Zipporah talking indoors. I was still waiting there when he came out.

'Back from your journey, Hur?' he asked.

'Yes. It was not a happy one.'

'I believe I am going to see a delegation this morning. Fellow travellers of yours.'

'They're not bad men.'

'Not bad,' he agreed. 'But how is the tribe to survive them?'

Later in the morning a crowd of a few hundred men arrived. Moses came out. And Aaron came to the door of his tent, wearing the breast plate of twelve precious stones. The delegation hissed and booed and one of them pointed to me and said, 'There's the backsliding bastard.'

Dathan spoke. 'We are sick,' he said, 'of the rule of your family. Yourself as leader and representative, as judge and law-giver. Your brother as chief priest. Is there really any need for him to be so supreme or you so tyrannous?'

'*I* am tyrannised,' Moses claimed. '*I*. More than any other tribesman.'

'Koreh is more worthy than your brother to be chief priest. Many men are more worthy than you as leader. So it's time for you to step down.'

Moses gestured towards the wall of his tent. 'You are welcome to argue that point with me in my tent.'

Very cleverly, Dathan implied that no honest man could risk stepping indoors with Moses.

'Do you think that I would murder you?' Moses called to the crowds.

'Yes,' said Dathan. 'It is not the first time you have murdered through your appointed judges.' And the crowd cheered at that.

'You are convinced,' Moses asked, 'that Yahweh would be content to see Koreh as chief priest? And as your leader one of a dozen other decent men other than me, a murderer?'

'I am pleased that you can manage,' Dathan admitted, 'to find the heart of our argument so quickly.'

'Let it be done like this then. Those who don't like me as a leader should make a separate camp, some distance away. Yahweh will choose between us one way or another. And quickly. If he does not, you will all know that he has not especially selected me. As for the Levites who support Koreh, you can all come to the sanctuary, bringing censers with you.'

Censers were very elegant metal baskets in which incense was burned. Most Levites had one. Either hammered out by smiths in the desert or extorted from the Egyptians in the old days of the ten plagues.

'If your incense pleases Yahweh,' Moses continued, 'you can expect to see me rejected. Perhaps I will turn leprous. Perhaps tumours will appear on my body.'

The prospect made the members of the conspiracy cheer.

'Only this,' Prince Moses said. 'Those who believe I am still Yahweh's man will stay in my camp and not once speak to the people of the other camp. When the thing is settled, then you can speak to one another, all knowing the one truth and the one leader. Only Koreh's Levites can enter the main camp, only then to stand with their censers in front of the tabernacle of Yahweh.'

'How long will it take?' Dathan asked. 'Before you admit – yes, the people of Koreh's faction are right and I am wrong?'

'I will be forced to admit it by my death or my leprous skin. Everyone will see. You will see. I will see. Everyone will know. All you men of Dathan's faction, and of Abiram's and of Koreh's are to remove themselves before sunset to a place further along the valley.' He smiled and made a little joke. 'You do not want my people corrupting your people.'

That night I developed a fever. For three days I was scarcely conscious. I remember terrifying dreams full of Yahweh's fire and the black tunics of the paid regulars of the north. On the second day a red rash covered my body. I began to rave. I can remember my skin burning with the rash. Though I did not know it, Koreh's Levites in front of the tabernacle were all falling down with the same fever. The few left healthy nursed the others. Koreh himself died. At the end of the week fifty of Koreh's Levites had gone down to the plague, which, in that tribe, would for ever after be called 'the fire'.

I think we must have all picked it up at the well at Horma, during our retreat. The water had tasted unhealthy at the time.

In the camp along the valley the same epidemic was raging. Aaron's Levites supplied food and water to Koreh's dying incense-burners but would not touch the flesh of their dying opponents.

It is easy to say, these people had picked up a disease during their northern escapade. Because they were now in a separate camp or on their own in the tabernacle, their plague did not spread to the Moses section of the tribe. Yet you have to admit, it did look as though Yahweh had made a strong selection between Koreh and Aaron, and Koreh was the hands-down loser.

And even more strange was what happened to Abiram's and Dathan's supporters further up the valley. At the end of the same week that I lay with the fever, at the end of the very same week that Koreh died of 'the fire', an earth tremor ran through the camp. It caused little damage in Moses' camp. A few tent-poles fell. But it was strongly felt further along the valley. The mountain of loose red sandstone which stood above the camp of Abiram and Dathan fell apart and tumbled on them. Dathan himself died spectacularly when the ground beneath him opened up so that he fell to his death, break-ing his back. We heard the noise of all this, and even the screams carried on the wind of the landslide. Most of the tents in that encampment were crushed. Young boys and girls who were out on the grassy plain with their flocks were the survivors, and a few mangled people from the outskirts of the camp. Such survivors as there were came into Moses' camp, looking stark. Aaron would say no prayer, make no sacrifice near the place where the disloyal tribesmen had suffered the mountain fall. It was as if they had never existed, except as names for the tribe and the race of the future to spit upon. I think their fate was a bit severe. But Yahweh, in his character of a loving vengeance, had certainly spoken up for Moses that week.

I was not a little appalled by what had happened. When I was better I went and sat in Moses' tent entrance. This time it was not an act of humility. I wanted to argue with him. Again I heard him chatting with Zipporah indoors.

Zipporah was saying, 'I took her soup. She didn't try to eat it straight off. She put it to one side. I wonder will she ever eat it.'

Zipporah was talking about her sister-in-law Miriam. Yahweh might be able to compel respect for his leader's wife, I thought rebelliously. But he couldn't make Miriam eat Zipporah's soup.

'She is very sick,' Moses said by way of excuse for his sister. 'You can't think too hardly of her.'

'I've never seen her eat anything prepared by my hand. She pretends to worry that I have left the meat full of blood.'

'That's her. She is a strong woman. And as they get old, the strong some-times get merely stubborn. You have to forgive her.'

This conversation on the question of whether a particular woman should eat another's soup, seemed nearly indecent to me. I seemed to be able still to feel in my blood the tremor that ran through the camp, the roar of the mountain and of the people who fell beneath it.

When he came out, I spoke to him. 'Do you feel pleased, Lord Moses?'

'Are you like that too?' he asked me.

'Like what?'

'Like the others. You think that *I* choose the punishments!'

I looked at him closely. All at once I could see that he was, in fact, a man in grief. He touched his temples. Perhaps there the noise of the crumbling mountain was embedded.

'I know,' he said. 'A god *Who Is* calls out to man, is easy to love. A god who brings the weak through the Sea of Reeds and drowns the army that hunts them. But a punishing god is harder to understand.'

'Are they both the same god?' I asked, not expecting an answer.

'It is hard to think what it is like to be Yahweh. But if you were the true god amongst all the false ones, and if to make your name known, you had chosen a tribe, and your name amongst men depended on whether that tribe took notice of you and accepted your love and your punishments, then perhaps you would sometimes be severe also. The nature of a king is something like the nature of Yahweh. And all good kings are severe. And only the mild and sentimental ones are dangerous. Do you want a mild and sentimental god?'

Very soon 'the fire' began to appear amongst people in Moses' camp. Moses and Aaron burnt incense continually in front of Yahweh's tent. For they believed that Yahweh might really intend to end the whole tribe with that plague.

According to Aaron, he was inside the sanctuary with Moses when he saw a ferocious block of fire land on the leader and encase him. He tried to reach his brother's hand and drag him out of this cage of burning light, but he could not. On instinct, he piled his censer with incense and went walking amongst the tents. He could hear the groans and ravings of those with the fever. But the camp filled up with the sweetness of the Levite incense. When he got back to the sanctuary, the light and fire were gone. Moses merely lay on the sandy floor of the sanctuary. There was a frothy scum on his lips, as if he had had a fit. Aaron could not wake him and had him carried back to his tent. There he slept the night and woke next day to news that the epidemic was abating. He had me called for. When I went into his tent he still lay on his pallet.

'Do you know what the god *Who Is* said to me when I was in his fire?' he asked me.

I felt a little uncomfortable at being told personally what went on between Yahweh and Prince Moses. 'No, I could not guess,' I confessed.

'Yahweh sang in my ear. *Abiram and Dathan and all the people of their tents, Koreh and all his Levites, they had become unfit for my sanctuary, unclean for my tribe. Yet who says that they are lost to me and have got no final mercy?'* Moses got up off his bed and put a hand on my shoulder. 'If I had been fit to speak at all, I would have said, that's exactly the opinion a friend of mine called Hur holds at this moment.'

My blood crept. I bowed my head. 'I stand warned,' I said.

'Please. I did not mean it as a threat.' You could see he was actually disappointed in me. 'I only wanted to tell you what happened to me there in the sanctuary. There is such a thing as friendship.'

'You must forgive me,' I said. I bowed to him again. The man had won me completely yet once more.

The Lawgiver sends out Embassies

Professional guides who came through Kadesh with caravans from the north told us that the cities of Canaan meant to send an army against the tribe of Israel. I can understand it in a way. If you have a tribe which, in spite of plagues, battles, disasters, still numbers thousands; if you let them settle in a valley like Kadesh, where they will breed well – then they will be a problem to you for twenty years and in the end they might even destroy you.

Therefore we were forced to travel westwards towards the Wilderness of Shur, where we spent a year in safety but on short rations. There were of course as many complaints as ever from the tribesmen. Thirst didn't worry Moses – he saw it all as part of a pattern, as a testing. But you can't expect ordinary people to see things that way. To them each thirsty day is the only day they care about.

Moses and I went looking for limestone again, and found it. The same sort of sink-holes as we'd found years before in the south.

Having found the place, he called it Waters of Rebellion, which I thought was a bit harsh of him. But there you are. History has no prizes for the average man, for the man of mildness, the man who calls people and events by soft names.

At last hard times brought us back to Kadesh. Life there was quite happy in fact. When we had been there earlier, there had been a lot of plagues and disasters because people did not know who was fit to be leader and who was fit to offer incense in the tabernacle. Now we had found out. Life was easier now, more settled and content. And as we lived there in our tents and amongst our flocks, never short of grass or water, many songs were composed and sung. And none of them said that Kadesh was our homeland. They all sang of Canaan, the land promised. Children born in Kadesh sang no other songs but these. They grew up taking for granted their right to the cedar forests and the valleys of Canaan.

But first the tribe must breed itself up to strength. We stayed in that valley a whole generation, till we were so numerous, till there were so many young men, that the valley could not quite hold them. In Kadesh, by sending young men on exploratory missions, Moses decided on a new way of entering the land promised. Instead of marching into those risky ravines in the north, he decided that the tribe, when the day of march came, would move eastwards, camping on the borders of the kingdom of Edom, moving through it as peacefully as possible, since the Edomites were a related race. Then northward into Moab which stood beside the sea called the Salt or the Dead. North again then to Nebo and over the Jordan into the hill towns of Canaan. You see, he had decided now to take Canaan from the flank, instead of front-on.

The only trouble was it would take longer. He used to say to me and anyone else my age, 'Our generation won't see Canaan. We were never single-minded enough . . .'

And I used to think, 'How single-minded do you have to be?'

In Kadesh Miriam got sick, bleeding from her kidneys. She was ashamed of this, since it made her ritually impure, and anyone who got the blood on them was ritually impure, too. Zipporah used to tend to her and clean her up.

'Arabs are good for something,' Zipporah would tease her.

'We all have our vanities,' Miriam said once. 'I have mine. I used to like to think I influenced him. I see I didn't influence him at all. I was born to do two simple things. Pack him in a hamper when he was a baby. Hide him in Pithom when he was a killer.'

'And my important thing,' Zipporah said, 'was to give him my body.'

When Miriam came to her last hour, Moses put on his blue and white priestly robes of leadership and stood in her tent, close enough for her to see him.

'It will never end, the struggle,' she said, struggling herself for breath. 'Even when we are in Canaan. And have taken the forfeit of all the people of Canaan.'

She meant by 'taken the forfeit', paid with their lives.

'Promise,' she said. 'Promise the forfeit will be taken.'

Moses bowed his head. 'None of them will be kept. They are all forfeit to Yahweh.' When he said it her breathing improved for a second.

'Look at him,' she ordered the rest of us weakly. 'Look at him.'

She died saying it. She had two tall daughters who looked like her as she was in the year I'd first met her. They began a mourning song and Moses took it up.

> *She is sweet dust,*
> *She is the dust of the valley floor, whose hands were*
> *the first hands I knew,*
> *and whose breasts were the first my mouth knew*
> *in its infancy.*

Very soon after the funeral, Moses began making his first diplomatic contacts with Edom. He called two well-known Levites as well as myself to his tent.

'The king of Edom is at present in Bozrah. You travel north-east from Kadesh. You can be sure that people – both spies and travelling men – have told him who we are, our numbers, what we expect of the future. He must know we do not want Edom, that we do not consider it is promised, that we do not wish to spend the young men of our tribe in taking it from him. He must have heard of the god *Who Is* and of what happened at the Sea of Reeds. Now say to him, we want leave to pass through your country. We will not march through fields or vineyards. We will not drink at the royal wells. We will travel by the king's road, not going off to the right or left until we've passed beyond your frontiers. The reason I send you, Hur, with these good men is that you have some knowledge of the wide world and used to speak, man to man, to Rameses and Merneptah.'

We came in dusty to Bozrah a week later. The royal villa stood on a mound in one corner of the city. It was mostly mud-brick, though the king had been able to afford some marble for columns and for putting a more royal face on the walls his citizens looked at. It was a crude place though, compared to what I had seen in Egypt. In the corridors stood idols of some bald god and a foul incense smoked in front of each statue.

The king was a heavy man. His face wasn't very sensitive. One of the Levites, whose name I deliberately keep back, began to tell the king that he must certainly have heard of their nation, Israel. That they had been slaves to the Egyptians. And about Yahweh, and the rest of it.

The king was such a barbarian that he had to have the speech translated for him by an official. When he had heard it all, he made a reply in some barbaric tongue.

The official told us, 'His Highness says he doesn't keep himself informed of the pedigree of every little desert tribe.'

I suggested that we should be permitted to march through. The tribe of Israel were his relatives. They intended no damage to his harvests or his waters.

The king made another speech.

'His Highness says no,' said the official.

We argued, but he threatened war, making chopping movements with his fat arm.

One of the Levites said, 'We do not consider the kingdom of Edom worth fighting you for.'

'I do not think,' said the official, 'it would be wise for me to pass on your opinion to His Highness.'

And His Highness sat, actually flicking grape seeds in our direction. But he did not want us to go. He offered us some of his women. After the journey we had had, it was too difficult to refuse them.

The girl I was appointed was dark, full, a nice little daughter of that corner of the world. But when she led me away to a bedroom, there was a statue of their fertility god, a monstrous stone member carved between his legs. First she oblated herself on this. That was obscene enough, even by the standards of an old worldling like me. It was only after she had finished ravishing herself on the statue, and then burning incense in front of it, that she came to me. Perhaps that way of making love suited the Edomites. But to me it was a pain in the stomach.

In fact, when we were riding away the next day, one of the notable Levites said something by which I knew he too had had the same weird experience with his girl.

'That's the trouble with these alien women,' he said. 'They are hard to resist. Especially if you come as a conqueror, I suppose. Yet they are full of foul rites. I mean, it would be nice to let them live, to have them there as servants, to taste them when you wanted. But five years, and they would have perverted the whole race.'

OVERLEAF 'When he had been stripped of all
clothes, they were put on Eleazar, his son,
who was then led to the edge of the cliff'

The other one said, 'They are already forfeit anyhow to Yahweh. Sad in a
way. But as you say, there is only one thing that makes soldiers spare foreign
women in battle. That's vanity.'

'When it comes down to it,' said the other, 'women are the ones who make
the worst heathens.'

The second one became even franker still. 'My girl felt all cold from lying
with that foreign god.'

We found the tribe east of Bozrah, near Oboth, near the border of the
kingdom. After the frightening experience with the Edomite girl, it was good
to be back with Joannah.

One morning, we came out of our tents to see an Edomite army lined up on
a slope to the north-east. Moses sent a few young Levites to say that we did
not want to fight Edom and would not pass through its country.

In this encampment, Aaron went into his last illness. This was near a
mountain called not Horeb but Hor. The mountain had some reputation as a
sacred place with Jethro's tribe.

It seemed better that the chief priest should die on top of a holy mountain
instead of in just another dry valley. So he was placed on a litter and carried

up there by members of his clan. Moses went, too.

I saw Aaron being carried out of camp. He had shrunk a lot. All the vanity of his young days was gone. Though he wore his official robes, they had been put on him that morning at great expense of pain. He kept saying in a little birdlike voice, 'Can you see Canaan? Can you see Canaan from up there?'

'With a good eye,' Moses lied. 'With a good eye you can see it.'

When the whole family got to the top, Moses – under the eye of the son – took the old man's robes off and put them on the son. Aaron's thin body had to be lifted. He could do nothing for himself. It was hard getting the long white and blue gowns off him. The little bells sewn on his blue garment tinkled madly and his breath rasped.

When he had been stripped of all clothes, they were put on Eleazar, his son, who was then led to the edge of the cliff. The tribe, far below, could see him and some raised their hands.

A tent was pitched for Aaron in that high place, and in the cold night he died.

The Lawgiver poises his Tribe

The next door kingdom to Edom on its northern border is called Moab. What the tribe did now was march around Edom, up a tortured valley that ran between the two kingdoms, along the eastern border of Moab and so to the river called Arnon.

There is a song sung of this river.

> *What he did by the Red Sea,*
> *he will do again in the valleys of Arnon.*
> *Among the mountain torrents that come down to rest in Ar,*
> *to flow peacefully through the lands of Moab.*

Now Joshua and other delegates were sent to Heshbon, north of Moab, to talk to King Sihon, tribal king of the area. They wanted that the tribe should be let through Sihon's territory so that we could cross the Jordan and so come at last into the hills of Canaan. He refused.

In the encampment near a well called Jasa, our camp took on a very military look. We dug a mound across its front. Since Yahweh's tent was amongst us, we kept ourselves ritually pure. No one had any doubt that that would help us in battle.

I stopped Moses one day as he was moving around the encampment with Joshua. 'You are sure it is time to start a war?' I asked him.

'It is our only way of getting into Canaan.'

'Then do you know what I think?'

'Tell me.'

'Your boys will win easily. Certainly King Sihon has professionals. Paid men. But what sort of professionals can a small king afford? Not very good ones. It will be tougher for us over in Canaan. All the regular soldiers that are worth their salt are over there. The army you will face here is made up of desert oafs. While you are trained in the Egyptian way. And have taught Joshua.'

He said very levelly, 'We will win, of course. But I would be grateful if you did not tell them it will be easy.'

King Sihon's army camped in front of us, down the valley. In the morning I watched with Moses as the front line of our tribal warriors marched out. They were singing, 'Yahweh is my shield and my cutting edge . . .'

It took only them to rout Sihon, only the front line. Sihon broke through nowhere. The boys with their slings were not needed and saw no combat. It was as easy as that for the young soldiers.

They marched into Heshbon and massacred men and drove everyone else out. They entered Mediba. They captured Baal-meon, a city named after the stone god my Edomite girl had introduced me to. Suddenly we had a walled city and many towns.

But Moses knew that if we were ever to cross into Canaan, we could not afford to be attacked from the right, from the north, where the kingdom of Bashan lay. So an army marched north with Joshua. As is now well known they met the army of King Og of Bashan near Edrei. He went the way of Sihon. The kings on that side of the Jordan couldn't match the Israeli Hapiru in battle.

The tribe, after all its years in the desert, did not now quite know what to do with its new cities. We pulled the walls down – they could always be rebuilt. We destroyed the shrines of the gods. Then we went on camping at Dibon close to the kingdom of Moab.

While we were camped there – it was a morning a few summers back – a man wearing very opulent clothes came riding down amongst our tents on a donkey. You could hear him some way off. He was chanting.

> *How fine are your tents, oh Israel.*
> *As the valleys are they spread out, as gardens by the*
> *river's side. As hanging gardens, as cedars on the*
> *river bank. Like a bucket brimming over at the well,*
> *see how their future spreads from one frontier to the next.*
> *The king that rules over them will rival Agag himself,*
> *and take away his kingdom from him . . .*

Then he fell from his donkey, fainting and frothing.

Next morning, when he had woken, he told an amazing story. He was a professional curser. He had been used for cursing people by the emperor of Assyria as well as by a lot of small kings and businessmen. He was so well known and so effective that he had a summer villa at Pethor in the north. There he liked to fish.

The king of Moab had seen the way Og and Sihon had gone so he sent three officials to speak to this professional curser, whose name, by the way, was Balaam. The officials had read a fairly hysterical letter from King Balak of Moab. He was offering a big price for an effective curse against the Israelis, and the chieftains of Midian had offered to put up some of the money, too.

The letter from Balak had read, 'If you looked, you would see there is a people that have come out from Egypt. They cover the face of the earth and they are camped over against me. I therefore require you to come immediately and curse for me this people, for they have already grown too strong for me. With your curse behind me I shall perhaps manage to drive them back into the wastelands. For I know well that whoever you bless turns out blessed, and whoever you curse, stays cursed.'

Balaam had been delighted with this commission and the promise of the fat fee. After treating the officials to dinner, he had gone into his study to look at his charts and his cabalistic diagrams. And while he was there, he said, he felt the room spin and his limbs threaten to tear away from his trunk. And he heard a voice, partly his own, partly that of anyone he had ever known, tell him that the Israeli people should not be cursed but blessed. Because a god *Who Is* had already blessed them.

So next morning with regret he refused to travel with the officials through Moab.

'What,' one of the officials asked, 'would you say if instead of a commission, Balak set up for you his nicest tortures and had your head on a plate?'

'A curse will work if it is allowed to. This one will not be allowed to.'

But the officials stayed on in his house all day, nagging and threatening him. So the next day he put a saddle on his donkey and headed south with them.

As they were moving through a pass in the frantic heat of late morning, Balaam's ass kept bridling. Balaam whipped her. The ass ground his leg up against one of the walls of the pass, and Balaam cursed it and yelled with pain. When he managed to get it to go on a few steps, it then fell down on the track. He got off and beat the animal fiercely.

'You'll make yourself giddy,' one of the officials yelled at him.

And then the ass spoke to him, in a voice like his own, but marred and strange.

'What have I done to you?' the ass asked. (Or so Balaam said it did.) 'Why do you have to beat me three times?'

Balaam began sweating. 'Who said that? Who spoke then? Was it really you? If I had a sword I'd thrust it straight into your rotten flanks.'

'Would you kill me? Aren't I your animal? Haven't you ridden me every day? And I never bridled?'

'You mock me. Do you hear? You mock me.'

'Did I ever mock you before?'

Then he fainted, as he had fainted the day he rode into our camp on his donkey. They took him to Balak nonetheless. When he was better, Balak took him onto the mountain of Baal and showed him our distant camp outside Dibon.

'It's no use. I can't curse them. A great god has already blessed them.'

'Come on then,' said Balak. 'Try.'

'It will take seven stone altars. On each of them a ram and a bullock has to be sacrificed.'

'All right. All right, it's worth it.'

But when the animals had been burnt on the stone altars, Balaam went into a fit and began to sing.

'Curse them?' he sang. 'I, when the god's curse does not light on them? I lay a ban on them, when the lord of life lays no ban on them? I will climb the high rocks to see them, the hills shall enlarge my view. For here is a people destined to dwell to one side, not counted among the muster roll of the ordinary nations.'

When he came to again, he found Balak was angry with him.

'I am the one that had the seizure,' Balaam answered. 'I only say what the god makes me say.'

Balak got a little contrite at this. There were few good cursers in the world, and if you made an enemy of one of them, you could well be the substance of his next curse.

'Listen,' he said. 'There is that mountain over there. Mount Phasga. From there you can only see part of the tribe. Perhaps if you do your sacrifices there . . .'

So Balaam tried Mount Phasga and the results were similar. And then he asked if he could try Mount Phegor. And on Phegor, too, Balak lost seven rams and seven bullocks.

'This is becoming a great expense and to no purpose,' Balak said.

'And to no purpose,' Balaam echoed.

'Didn't I send for you to curse my enemies, and now you have blessed them three times? I meant to give you a royal honour, but this god that speaks through you has spoiled all that.'

'Didn't I warn the messengers you sent?'

Now even on the day he told this story in our camp at Dibon, Balaam was in two minds. He resented what this foreign god had done to him, and the words it had put in his mouth. And on the second day he found young men surrounding his donkey, talking to it in comic ways.

'Your excellency, did the king of Moab lend you any of his whores? What was it like in the palace in which you grew up?' That sort of thing.

Being a vain man, he was very distressed. When he went away, back to the north, to his villa and his fish, he was very angry at the god of the ungrateful Israelis.

So, at his own expense and by his own influence, he set up a number of holy Canaanite whores and sent them to the camp the following year while we were near Sittim. The whores settled down in a quarter of the wrecked city. Whenever an Israeli man came to them, they first performed the rite with their stone gods. Surprisingly, some men liked this.

One night Phineas, Aaron's grandson, followed a fashionable young man called Zambri into the quarters of one of these women. The boy's father was a chief of clan Simeon. I say he was fashionable, because everyone was dressing better now, what with the loot from our many towns. The whore's name was Cozbi. Phineas waited outside. He was aware that Zambri himself was burning incense to the god.

When that rite was over and the two, Zambri and Cozbi, were enmeshed with each other, Phineas opened the door. They looked up. There is nothing more terrible than a messenger from Yahweh. With a sword in his hand. Before Zambri had moved, Phineas had run the sword through his genitals and bowels and into the woman's womb. It must have been terrible, the two of them stuck together, writhing in a way they had not expected.

The next night, execution squads of Levites went round dealing death to all the sacred whores Balaam had sent. And very soon, after the Israelis had fought a battle with the desert Midianites, Balaam was found in the tent of one of the sheiks and was executed on the spot.

Let me say, that I was never around when these people who were forfeit to Yahweh were treated to the sharp edge of Israel's weapons.

The Lawgiver dies

In the very last years of the leader's life a change came in the way the tribe lived. Now the cities of Heshbon and Dibon had Israelis living in them. And people were asking for grants of land, and growing crops in the lowlands beneath Nebo.

It all sounds grand. Cities occupied, lands farmed, races exterminated with their whores and their gods. In fact Heshbon was a little hole of a place. On this side of the Jordan the kingdoms had been such that a cunning race of maybe ten thousand tribesmen were able to take the cities and chew up their paltry armies. As Moses said, it will be harder on the other side of Jordan, where the cities were real cities and the kings real kings and the armies had the respect even of the Egyptians.

But although there were some signs we would one day soon turn into townsmen and farmers, most of us still lived in a great camp near Mount Nebo. The king of Moab looked down from his mountains at us but did not come near. He bribed little desert chieftains to attack, and Joshua's army ate them whole.

As the old died in this camp, Joannah and I lived on. You couldn't even say we had bad health. Sometimes Moses would visit us to talk to us, for there were not many of his age left standing.

'They want me to give the order. Joshua does, Caleb. They want to move over the river in the direction of Jericho. Jericho is said to be a fair city. It takes two hours to walk around its walls. So our spies say.'

'Why don't you give the order?'

'Because I am not meant to see Canaan. I know it. I am meant to die on this side.'

At least he was delicate enough not to tell Joannah and me that we were meant to die on this wilder side of Jordan also.

'You can't be sure of any of these things,' I would tell him.

'Don't tell me that,' he chuckled. 'All my life I have suffered from being sure about things.'

'I suppose so.'

He used to tease me. 'You've always thought I was half mad. Even half evil. You wonder, why does an Egyptian prince – or one that used to be that – why does he watch over the tribal army as it makes whole towns pay the forfeit to Yahweh?'

'In those months he kept gathering the
entire tribe in front of the tent of Yahweh
and lecturing them'

The Lawgiver dies

'Well,' I would say, 'I suppose even the Egyptians treat beaten races that
way. They think their enemies are forfeit to Ra or Horus.'

'This people didn't come to the borders of Canaan to be seduced by a few
desert whores. It could happen. The whole tribe, there is some weakness at
its core. And after I'm gone – what?'

'There will still be Yahweh. There will still be Joshua.'

He grunted. 'Yes. I suppose it's this. Life is so sweet. Even for me. I've
often wanted to sink into the earth. Yet I have had the passion for Yahweh.
And I have had Zipporah's sweet body in its flower. And now in my old age,
I can afford friends, and go from tent to tent chatting. And from Nebo I can
see the olive mountains of Canaan. It is all so sweet. Hur, I don't want to go.'

'Neither do I,' I said sincerely.

In those months he kept gathering the entire tribe in front of the tent of
Yahweh and lecturing them. People began to think it a bit of a joke. It was as
if he didn't remember that he himself had appointed judges and tribal leaders

and generals. And that they were men of some talent. And that the tribe was working nearly as well as even he could expect.

One day he had a sort of seizure, and one side of his mouth was paralysed. He still went on lecturing. He decided himself the case of the tribe of Ruben and Gad and Manasseh.

He sat in front of the tent of Yahweh. The tribal leaders of these three tribes came forward to him. Their spokesman spoke.

'Ruben and Gad have very good flocks. Very numerous. Manasseh, too, is well endowed. Now here is Ataroth . . .' (this was the name of a town) . . .' 'here are Dibon and Jazer and Nemra and Heshbon and Eleale and Saban and Nebo and Beon, all given to us by Yahweh, into the hands of Israel at the first attack. But all of this is good grazing land. Prince Moses, we have many beasts to feed and we ask a favour of you. Give us this land as our share, instead of making us cross the Jordan to win land over there.'

Moses spoke savagely out of his crippled mouth. 'What? Are your brothers to go and fight while you sit idle here? Would you dampen the morale of the Israelis, so that they no longer have the courage to cross over into that land which Yahweh means to give to them? After all, what you are asking is exactly what your fathers asked in Kadesh when the spies came back from Canaan. Joshua and Caleb said that Canaan was ready for us like fruit on a tree. Your fathers said no, Kadesh was good enough for them. Later they changed their minds, but that was their first message: Kadesh was good enough for them. But Kadesh was not promised and these pastures were not promised. Yet they are good enough for you.'

The tribal leaders persisted.

'We intend only to build folds for our sheep, corrals for our cattle and cities where our children can stay safely. Then we like the others will go ahead. Armed and buckled up for battle, in the vanguard if you like. Until we have won territories for the others. We have to have walled towns to protect our children and our possessions from sudden attack from Moab, and from the Midianites of the desert. But our fighting men will not come back to these homes of ours till the other Israelis have won their shares. And we will not demand any lands on the other side of Jordan, once we have our share guaranteed to us on this side.'

'I will have to think of this question. You will see much sweet land over there. When you know it is to go to other clans, how will you feel then?'

One of the tribal leaders went red in the face. He felt offended. I don't blame him. 'Some men,' he said, 'in their old age, think they are the only men on earth who keep their word. But Ruben and Gad and some of the families of Manasseh, perhaps they keep their word, too.'

Old Prince Moses laughed publicly. It was a luxury he had never been able to afford before. 'I will let you know. But I think, no.'

Three days later, in the same place, he gave his judgment.

'If you take these lands here from Edrei down to Aroer, then you must keep your young men in the army of our race. And it will not be you who decide what numbers of men will march. The generals will decide it justly for you. Leaving you enough to protect your towns.'

One of the tribal leaders said, 'It will be a matter of pride with us.'

In his final illness, he stood up one day and sang a song about Yahweh the vengeance. And he ran the tribe down, so that people wept in front of him, justly hurt.

'A people so well loved,' he ranted. 'And now pampered, they would throw off the yoke. Pampered, full fed, swollen with pride, they give up that great maker, they revolt against Yahweh who saved them in Egypt and in the desert . . .'

It was sad to watch. Joannah cried beside me. At last, young Levites took him home to his bed.

Then, a day or so later, he would say the most loving things.

'See where Yahweh comes forth from Sinai where he rises high above the hills of Edom, and dawns on us from Mount Pharam. Thousands of his consecrated people are round him, and on his right hand his law shines on them like fire. How he loves these tribes of his.' And he would say complimentary things of the clan of Ruben, of Judah, of Levi, of Benjamin, of Joseph and Zabulon. And of Gad, even though that clan had chosen to live east of Jordan.

Zipporah now was a silent old woman sitting in a corner. One morning he kissed her.

'Put me on a litter, the way my brother Aaron was treated. Put on my official clothes, don't worry if the effort of the sleeves seems to be too much for me. Put them on anyhow. I want my sons to carry me on top of Nebo. Tell Joshua to come. And send for Hur.'

I came to his tent. I could still walk fairly fast. The last fast walker of my generation in that tribe.

'Hur, my brother,' he said. 'Come up with me. Die with me up there. Where we ought to die. Looking across at Canaan.'

The eyes worked on me as they had the first day I was captured. The idea of death on Nebo pulled at me, like tides pulling on a boat. I very nearly said yes. 'I would like to,' I said weeping. 'But I can't say no to my life.'

'It's easier', he said, 'Easier than you think once you start slipping . . .'

'But I don't want to slip. Not yet. Not into death.'

I felt I was arguing for my life. Suddenly his eyes gave up pulling on me.

'It's all right,' he said. 'Go back to your tent.'

Now that he was going up Nebo to die, the tribe followed him wailing to the base of the hill. It is reported that he said, 'What, no dust? No stones?' He meant no dust thrown after him, no stones hurled at his head. 'Dust and stones used to be more the fashion than tears.'

But how the people wailed.

I write all this on our farm near Jericho. For Joannah and I crossed into Jericho. We are still healthy.

Only sometimes she says to me, 'Do you think Yahweh neglected to take me to him while I was east of Jordan? Do you think he neglects me because I married you?

'I am circumcised,' I say. 'There's nothing wrong with me.'

But she goes on worrying about why she is living. And continues healthy from day to day. She's a typical Israeli.